John H. Thompson

HOOKED ON
AMERICAN
HISTORY!

101 Crossword Puzzle Activities
Based on U.S. History from
Pre-Exploration to the 1990's

THE CENTER FOR APPLIED
RESEARCH IN EDUCATION
West Nyack, New York 10995

10 9 8 7 6 5 4 3 2 1

Library of Congress Cataloging-in-Publication Data

Thompson, John H.
    Hooked on American history! : 101 crossword puzzle activities
based on U.S. history from pre-exploration to the 1990's / John H.
Thompson.
      p.   cm.
  ISBN 0-87628-402-0
    1. United States—History—Miscellanea. 2. Crossword puzzles.
I. Title.
E179.T45 1993
973—dc20   93-29991
                                                CIP

ISBN 0-87628-402-0

**The Center for Applied
Research in Education**
Business Information & Publishing Division
West Nyack, NY 10095

Simon & Schuster, A Paramount Communications Company

Printed in the United States of America

About *Hooked on American History!*

The purpose of this resource is to help you meet one of the daily challenges that faces any teacher today—the task of creating lessons that are informative and interesting for your students, but not time-consuming for you to prepare. Specifically, the goals of *Hooked on American History!* are:

- to save the instructor valuable time in lesson preparation
- to provide information and ideas that challenge all students
- to enliven historical facts with activities that are enjoyable and meaningful to students
- to encourage correct spelling skills and vocabulary mastery

With this unique collection of ready-to-use activities at your fingertips, you can spark involvement in students of varying abilities while also shortening your lesson planning by hours!

Included are 101 reproducible crossword puzzle activities appropriate for students in grades 7–12. The crosswords cover each era of American History, for example: The Indians, The Explorers, The Colonies, The Wars, The Roaring 20's on through the 50's, 60's, 70's, and 80's. Other puzzles cover topics such as Famous American Names, Vocabulary Words in American History, Women in American History, Important Years in American History, and even Nicknames.

For quick access and easy use, the puzzles are presented in chronological order, numbered consecutively, and printed in a big 8¼" × 11" spiral-bound format. Each is ready to be photocopied as many times as you need it for use with individual students, small groups, or an entire class. Moreover, complete answer keys are provided at the end of the book, and these may also be photocopied and placed at a central location if you wish to permit students to check their own work.

You'll find the activities in this versatile teaching resource have many possible uses. For example, they may serve as homework assignments, extra-credit activities, make-up tests, emergency or daily lesson plans, textbook reviews, or individual workbooks. Few students can resist the challenge of solving puzzles. Crosswords motivate even unexcited and less capable students and provide excellent reinforcement for overachievers who finish other class assignments ahead of schedule. Moreover, they offer a great break in the daily routine.

I have found the most productive uses of these activities are to arouse students' interest at the beginning of a history unit and to review information at the end of a lesson. Students learn while having fun. Historical events, people, and places take on new life and meaning when they become part of a puzzle!

John H. Thompson

About the Author

John Thompson received his B.A. in English and History from East Tennessee State University in Johnson City. He has been a teacher in the public schools of Tennessee, Arizona, and Virginia for over 20 years and has taught English, American Government, Economics, Geography, International Relations, World History, and United States History. His students have been diverse also, ranging in level from remedial eighth graders to adults and coming from many ethnic groups.

In addition to his classroom teaching experience, Mr. Thompson has been a successful coach. He is presently teaching history at Churchland High School in Portsmouth, Virginia.

Contents

Puzzle
Number   Puzzle Title

101 Crossword Puzzle Activities Based on U.S. History from Pre-Exploration to the 1990's

1. THE FIRST AMERICANS

ACROSS:

4. Capital of the Incas
6. River in Alaska
8. Indians of Peru
11. Type of Indian housing *(variation of spelling)*
13. Oldest inhabited town in the U.S.
15. Origin of the American Indian
17. Southeastern Indians
20. Society in which women hold power
21. Mountains of South America
23. Scientist who studies plants
24. Great Lakes Indians
25. Flat-topped hill
26. Sun-dried clay bricks
28. Method of dating, _____ 14
29. Indians of Alaska
31. Scientist who studies land formations
32. Land of the Incas
34. Indian winter celebration
36. Indians of Virginia

38. Continent the Indians came from
41. _____ pole
43. Indian "money"
44. Northwestern Indians
46. New Spain
47. Southeastern Indians
49. Origin of the American Indian
51. Triangular shaped religious temple
52. Capital of the Mayas
56. Plains Indians
58. Buffalo
62. Type of Indian housing
63. Southwestern Indians
64. Northwestern Indians
67. Northeastern Indians
70. Animal hunted by the Plains Indians
71. Land of the Aztecs
72. Indian harvest celebration
73. Indians of Central America

DOWN:

1. Southwestern Indians
2. Explorer who named the Indians
3. Scientist who studies human behavior
5. Plains Indians
7. Strait separating Alaska from Asia
9. Scientist who studies ancient peoples
10. Plains Indians
11. Carved wooden statue
12. Indian "peace pipe"
14. Southeastern Indians
16. Northeastern Indians
18. Separated from America by the Bering Strait
19. Indians led by Montezuma
22. Indians of Florida
27. Type of Indian housing
30. Indian chiefs
33. Large ice mass
35. Northwestern Indians
37. Southwestern Indians

39. Plains Indians
40. Southwestern Indians
42. Last Indians to migrate to America
45. Indian spirit doll
46. Indians of Central America
48. Type of Indian housing
50. Name given to Americans by Columbus
51. Southwestern Indians
53. Northeastern Indians
54. Indians of Mexico
55. Northwestern Indians
57. Type of Indian housing
59. Mountains of North America
60. Great Lakes Indians
61. The first Americans
65. Indian corn
66. Tall carved statue of wood
68. Southwestern Indians
69. Great Lakes Indian tribe

Name _____ Date _____

1. The First Americans

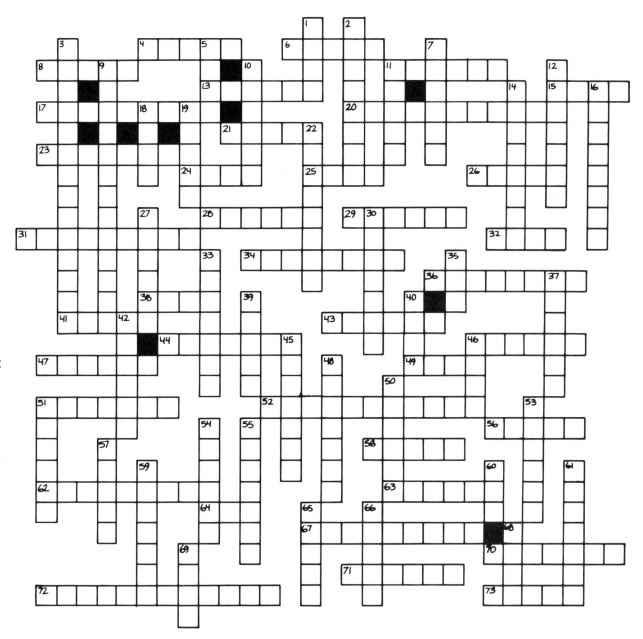

2. SPANISH EXPLORATION IN THE NEW WORLD

ACROSS:

3. Name given to the natives of America by Columbus
5. American-born Spaniards
6. Southwest Indians discovered by Coronado
10. Man for which America is named
14. Number of voyages made to America by Columbus
15. Spanish explorer of southeast North America
16. Land of the Incas
18. A ship of Columbus's first exploration
19. First permanent Spanish settlement in North America
20. Home of Christopher Columbus
21. Island explored by Columbus
23. _____, Pinta, and Santa Maria
24. Explorer who discovered the New World was not a part of Asia
26. Capital of Peru
27. Indians conquered by Pizarro
29. First Spanish explorer to see the Pacific Ocean
30. First Spanish explorer to sail the Pacific Ocean
31. Spanish conquerer of the Aztecs
32. First explorer for Spain
37. First Spanish king to send slaves to the New World
38. A ship of Columbus's first exploration

40. Southwest Indians discovered by Coronado
41. Southwest Indians discovered by Coronado
42. A ship of Columbus's first exploration (two words)
44. Capital of the Incas
47. Children of the Spanish and Native Americans
49. Island explored by Columbus
50. Spanish queen who financed Columbus
53. Famous Spanish missionary in America
55. Home of Amerigo Vespucci
56. Father _____
57. Spanish children born in America
62. Spanish explorer of Florida
64. Amerigo _____
65. Local leaders of Spanish colonies in America
68. Nina, _____, and Santa Maria
70. Spanish explorer of Panama
71. Spanish seeker of the Fountain of Youth
77. Sister ship of the Santa Maria
78. Spanish conquerer of Mexico
79. Spanish forts in America
80. Spanish conquerer of the Incas
81. Christopher _____
82. Indians conquered by Cortes

DOWN:

1. Spanish king who financed Columbus
2. Spanish explorer buried in the Mississippi River
4. Spanish explorer of southwest North America
5. Spanish explorer who discovered the Grand Canyon
7. Spanish forts
8. Spanish soldiers in America
9. Animals brought to America by Columbus
11. Land conquered by Pizarro
12. Spanish conquerer of Mexico
13. Island discovered by Columbus
17. Indians conquered by the Spanish
22. Native Americans
24. Spanish towns in America
25. Spanish explorers whose crew sailed around the world
28. Spanish explorer of southwest North America
33. Leader of the Aztecs
34. Indians of Central America
35. Sister ship of the Santa Maria
36. Land explored by Balboa
37. Spanish conquerer of the Aztecs
38. Spanish explorer of South America

39. Indians of Mexico
43. Spanish explorer who named Florida
45. Name that Columbus gave to native Americans
46. Central American Indians
48. Land of the Aztecs
51. _____ and Isabella
52. Object of Spanish exploration in Mexico
54. Land conquered by Cortes
58. Capital of the Incas
59. Spanish explorer of Florida
60. Island discovered by Columbus
61. Object of Spanish exploration in Peru
63. Smallest ship of Columbus's first exploration
66. Object of Spanish exploration in Mexico
67. Isthmus between North and South America
69. Indians ruled by Montezuma
72. Indians conquered by Pizarro
73. Number of explorations made by Columbus
74. Land of the Incas
75. Ship of Columbus's first exploration
76. _____, Peru

Name _____ Date _____

2. Spanish Exploration in the New World

3. FRENCH EXPLORATION IN THE NEW WORLD

ACROSS:

3. French explorer of the St. Lawrence River
6. French explorer of the Mississippi River
8. Object of French profit in America
10. Animal trapped by the French explorers
11. River explored by LaSalle
12. Great Lake explored by France
14. French king during the Age of Exploration
15. Great Lake explored by France
20. French king for whom the Louisiana Territory was named
22. French settlement in Canada
26. St. _____ River
29. Native country of Verrazano
30. King _____ XIII
31. Home of Verrazano
32. _____ Orleans
33. _____ Lakes
34. _____ of Exploration
37. The _____ Lakes
39. French name for Canada *(two words)*
40. Device for catching fish
42. Object of French profit in the Louisiana Territory
43. French explorer of the Mississippi River
45. _____ France
46. Object of French profit in the New World
47. _____ Lawrence River
52. French fur trappers
54. _____ Cartier
55. First explorer for France
56. French leader who began exploration
58. French explorer who founded Quebec
62. _____ Joliet
64. _____ Lawrence River *(abbr.)*
65. Indian name for northern America
66. River explored by France
68. King _____ XIV
69. _____ Orleans
70. Great _____
72. _____ Lawrence River *(abbr.)*
73. The _____ Lakes

DOWN:

1. Marquette and _____
2. The _____ Lakes
4. Great Lake explored by France
5. _____ de Champlain
7. Lake _____
9. Object of French profit in Canada
13. One of the Great Lakes
16. French settlement on the Mississippi River
17. New _____
18. French missionaries in America
19. _____ and Joliet
21. Native country of Verrazano
23. French explorer who named the Louisiana Territory
24. French fur trappers and hunters
25. Religion of Jacques Marquette
27. First French settlement in the New World
28. Land north of the Great Lakes
32. _____ Orleans
35. Great Lake explored by France
36. One of the first French explorers
38. St. Lawrence _____
41. Largest river in the Louisiana Territory
44. French settlement founded by Champlain
48. _____ Marquette
49. New _____
50. King _____ I
51. First European to see New York harbor
52. Lake named for a French explorer
53. Beaver _____
57. French king for whom the Louisiana Territory was named
59. One of the Great Lakes
60. First French interest in the New World
61. French explorer who reached the mouth of the Mississippi River
63. Native country of Verrazano
67. Object of French profit in the New World
71. _____ Lawrence River *(abbr.)*

3. French Exploration in the New World

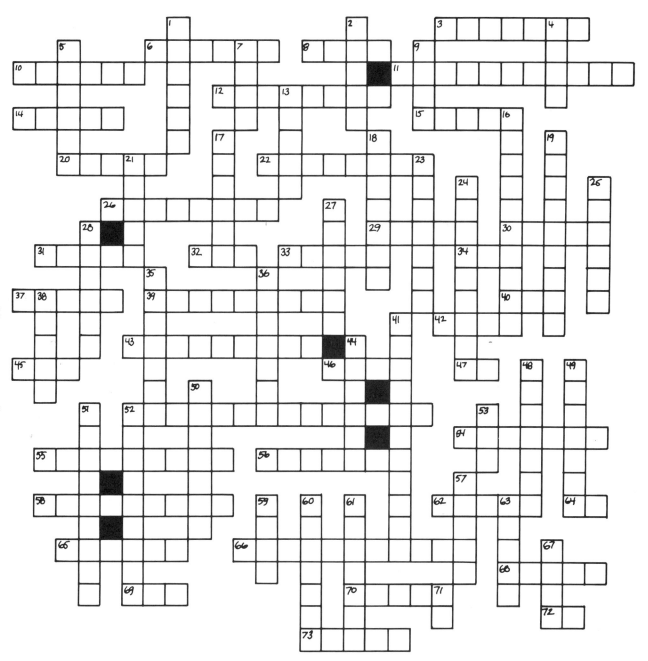

4. ENGLISH EXPLORATION IN THE NEW WORLD

ACROSS:

1. Sir _____ Drake
5. British leader of Roanoke Island
7. Ocean crossed by Sir Francis Drake
8. Objective of British pirates
10. _____ Cabot
15. Objective of British "seadogs"
17. First English baby born in the New World (last name)
18. _____ Walter Raleigh
19. Golden _____
20. British sea pirate
21. Sir _____ Drake
23. _____ Hawkins
25. _____ Carolina
26. Roanoke Island (abbr.)
28. Present location of Roanoke Island
29. Objective of British pirates
30. North Carolina (abbr.)
32. Virginia (abbr.)
33. British pirates' nickname
34. _____ Hind
35. Roanoke Island (abbr.)
36. British title of nobility
38. "Lost Colony" clue (abbr.)
41. Sir _____ Raleigh

43. British king who began exploration
45. _____ Walter Raleigh
46. North Carolina (abbr.)
47. First explorer to claim part of North America for England
49. Virginia _____
50. _____ White
53. Roanoke Island leader
55. British queen who began American colonization
56. British explorer who reached Newfoundland
57. _____ Francis Drake
58. British title of knighthood
59. First British explorer to bring slaves to the New World
62. Native country of John Cabot
64. "_____dogs"
65. Leader of the unsuccessful British colony
66. Golden _____
67. Same as 62 across
68. _____ Thomas Cavendish
70. British queen during the Age of Exploration

DOWN:

2. "Lost Colony" clue (abbr.)
3. The Golden _____
4. _____ Walter Raleigh
6. Same as 66 across
8. Pirate ship of Sir Francis Drake
9. First British explorer to cross the Pacific Ocean
11. _____ Hudson
12. British explorer of eastern Canada
13. "Lost Colony" clue
14. _____ Dare
16. Nickname of the Roanoke Island colony
19. British sea pirate
22. Carving on a Roanoke Island tree
24. British sea pirate
25. "Lost Colony" present location
27. British explorer in search of a Northwest Passage
31. "_____ Colony"
35. Unsuccessful British colony in America

37. First explorer for England
39. The _____ Hind
40. First British explorer to sail around the world
42. Unsuccessful British colony (abbr.)
44. Explorer who started the first British colony in America
48. "The _____ Colony"
51. King _____ VII
52. British king during the Age of Exploration
53. Sir _____ Raleigh
54. _____ Carolina
56. Carving on the "Lost Colony" tree
58. British rival during the Age of Exploration
60. "Lost Colony" leader
61. Roanoke Island location (abbr.)
63. "_____ Colony"
69. Hudson _____

4. English Exploration in the New World

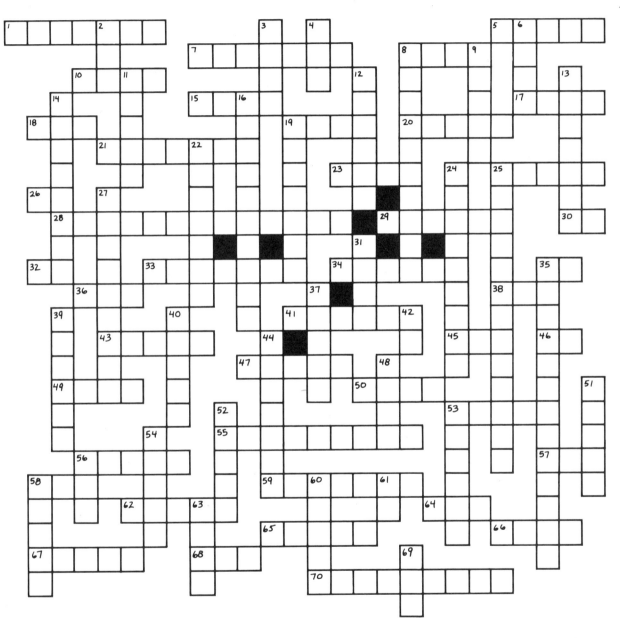

5. THE FIRST AMERICAN SETTLEMENTS

ACROSS:

6. _____ Buras
7. Massachusetts peninsula
11. "No _____, no eat"
12. Daughter of Powhatan
13. Equipment given to freed indentured servants (two words)
15. Disease that affected the Pilgrims
16. Joint-stock company that started the Massachusetts colony
18. The Church of England
20. _____ Burrows
21. Chief of the Indians in Virginia
23. First Dutch settlement in America
26. Virginia settler who introduced tobacco
28. Plymouth _____
29. _____ Buras
33. Massachusetts _____ Company
35. Captain of the Godspeed
36. Capital of the Massachusetts Bay Colony
38. Contract of work for passage to America
42. "No work, no _____"
43. New England political representatives
44. Husband of Pocahontas
48. Capital of England
49. One of the first women to Virginia
50. English settlers of Massachusetts
51. One of the first ships to Jamestown
53. _____ right system
55. Author of "no work, no eat"
57. Father of Puritanism
58. Led a rebellion of Virginia farmers
59. Leader of the Massachusetts Puritans
60. Freedom _____
61. _____ Constant
65. Virginia political representatives
67. Father of Calvinism
69. Permit to found a colony
72. Colony founded by the London Company
73. _____ Winthrop
76. Son of King James
78. "Black _____"
80. Island purchased from the Indians
82. Cape _____
83. _____ University
85. Indian friend of the Pilgrims
86. First settlement in Virginia
88. New Sweden settlers
89. Joint-stock company that started Virginia
90. Ship of the Pilgrims

DOWN:

1. Leader of the Jamestown settlement
2. _____ Burrows
3. Virginia land grant system (two words)
4. English name of Pocahontas
5. Dutch settlement at Albany, New York
7. The Mayflower _____
8. One of the first ships to Jamestown
9. "No work, no _____"
10. Husband of Pocahontas
12. Religious settlers of Massachusetts
14. Leader of the Massachusetts settlers
16. _____ Rock
17. Colonial Virginia governor
19. Dutch land grant system
21. Indian wife of John Rolfe
22. Young man learning a trade
24. "Freedom _____"
25. Led a rebellion of Virginia farmers
27. Indians of Massachusetts
30. _____ Rolfe
31. British king when Jamestown was founded
32. Cash crop of Virginia
34. _____ Smith
37. English king who started American colonization
39. Country that sent the most settlers to North America
40. Harvest celebration in Massachusetts
41. Laws for Black Virginians (two words)
45. One of the first ships in Jamestown
46. Joint-stock company in Virginia
47. _____ Standish
49. Leader of the Plymouth Colony
52. Tisquantum
54. Colony founded by the Pilgrims
56. New England college founded by the Puritans
62. One of the first women in Virginia
64. King _____
66. Jamestown leader
68. First English colony in America
70. Colonial clothing
71. First governor of the Massachusetts Bay Colony
74. Indentured _____
75. Colonial Massachusetts governor
77. Disease affecting the Jamestown settlers
79. Fort _____
81. Settlers in New Amsterdam
84. "No work, no _____"
87. _____ Amsterdam

© 1993 by The Center for Applied Research in Education

5. The First American Settlements

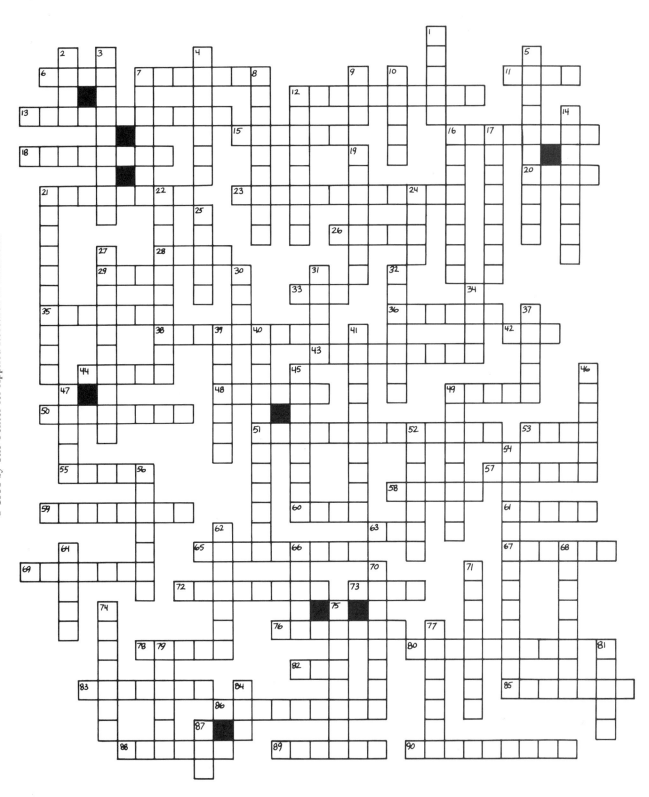

6. THE ORIGINAL THIRTEEN COLONIES

ACROSS:

3. Colony founded for Catholics *(abbr.)*
5. Colony founded for Quakers *(abbr.)*
6. English king who granted land for Maryland
9. Colony founded by John Wheelwright *(abbr.)*
12. The study of God
13. Large southern farm
14. Colony taken from the Dutch *(abbr.)*
16. Major seaport in South Carolina
19. Founder of Connecticut
20. Capital of New York
21. A religious belief rejected by the majority
23. _____ Island
24. Colony governed by William Penn
27. Capital of Connecticut
29. Staple crop
30. Rice colony *(abbr.)*
31. Staple crop
32. Namesake of Maryland
33. Colony ruled by Lord Berkeley *(abbr.)*

34. Tobacco colony *(abbr.)*
36. Capital of North Carolina
39. Colony founded by John Locke *(abbr.)*
41. Founder of Rhode Island
43. Tobacco colony *(abbr.)*
44. The freest of all the British colonies
45. Hello
46. Smallest colony *(abbr.)*
47. Religious people of Massachusetts
48. The last colony to be founded *(abbr.)*
50. Colony founded by John Locke *(abbr.)*
51. Capital of Rhode Island
53. Rice colony *(abbr.)*
55. British king who granted land for Virginia
56. City of brotherly love
58. Island in New York
62. _____ Baltimore
64. Buffer colony *(abbr.)*
65. Founder of the Carolinas
67. Religious people of Maryland
68. Founder of Pennsylvania

DOWN:

1. Founder of New Jersey
2. Founder of Georgia
4. Colony originally part of Pennsylvania
5. Founder of Delaware
6. Capital of New Hampshire
7. Capital of Georgia
8. Founder of Pennsylvania
9. Empire State *(abbr.)*
10. Major seaport of Georgia
11. Staple crop
15. James, Duke of _____
17. Capital of New Jersey
18. River dividing Maryland and Virginia
22. Area claimed by Massachusetts *(abbr.)*
25. Capital of Maryland
26. Capital of Pennsylvania
28. Capital of Delaware
29. Capital of South Carolina
33. Indians of Rhode Island

35. Founder of Maryland
36. Smallest colony *(abbr.)*
37. River in New York
38. Colonial capital of Virginia
40. Staple crop
42. Capital of Massachusetts
44. Colony founded by Roger Williams *(abbr.)*
45. Theologian banished from Massachusetts
49. Colony with the Toleration Act
52. The first colony *(abbr.)*
54. Colony founded by Lord Baltimore *(abbr.)*
57. River in Virginia
59. _____ Hutchinson
60. Tobacco colony *(abbr.)*
61. Colony originally owned by the Swedish *(abbr.)*
63. Colony led by Peter Minuit
66. Last colony to be founded *(abbr.)*

6. The Original Thirteen Colonies

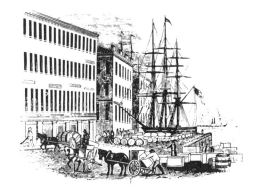

7. THE FRENCH AND INDIAN WAR

ACROSS:

6. Fort Louisbourgh was located on Cape _____ Island
7. Final battle of the war
9. Proposed the Albany Plan of Union
13. Royal governor of Virginia
14. City that was originally Fort Duquesne
15. Indian allies of the French
18. _____ Breton Island
21. Chief of the Mohawk Indians
22. British fort in the Ohio Territory

25. In Europe, the conflict was called The _____ Years' War
27. Plains of _____
28. River originally claimed by France
30. French fort in the Ohio Territory
31. Turning point in the war
33. French general killed at Quebec
36. Capital of England
38. River that helps form the Ohio River
39. Colonial leader in the war

DOWN:

1. River that helps form the Ohio River
2. British general
3. French fort captured by the colonists in 1745
4. River dividing French and British territory
5. Capital of France
8. British soldiers
10. St. _____ River
11. The Allegheny and Monongahela Rivers form the _____ River
12. British Prime Minister
16. Home of George Washington

17. British name for Fort Duquesne
19. French port at the mouth of the Mississippi River
20. British king
23. _____ Lawrence River (abbr.)
24. Indian allies of the British
26. Great Lake near the Ohio Territory
29. _____ of Abraham
32. British general killed at Quebec
34. _____ Franklin
35. Territory fought over in the French and Indian War
37. _____ Orleans

© 1993 by The Center for Applied Research in Education

7. The French and Indian War

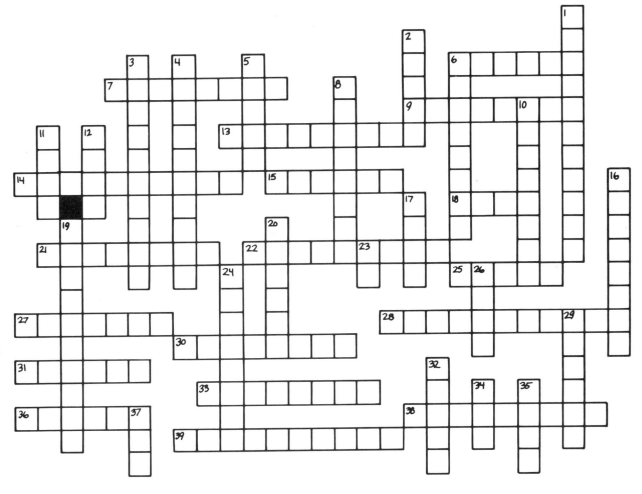

8. THE IDEA OF LIBERTY

ACROSS:

4. Chief of the Ottawa Indians
8. Colony founded for Catholics *(abbr.)*
10. King of England
12. A leader of the Continental Congress
13. A leader of the Continental Congress
14. "We must indeed all hang together, or most assuredly, we shall hang separately"
16. First American to die in the struggle with England
18. British governor of Massachusetts
19. British general at Bunker Hill
21. Colonial leader at the Battle of Quebec
24. Named the "Boston Massacre"
25. Rice colony *(abbr.)*
26. Smallest colony *(abbr.)*
28. "The British are coming"
29. British general in the colonies
30. Tobacco colony *(abbr.)*

31. Colonial patriot who warned of British attack
32. Author of the Declaration of Independence
33. First state *(abbr.)*
34. Connecticut *(abbr.)*
35. Buffer colony *(abbr.)*
38. Colonial patriot who warned of British attack
39. "Letters from a Farmer in Pennsylvania to the Inhabitants of the British Colonies"
42. First colony *(abbr.)*
44. "Give me Liberty, or give me death"
45. First New England colony *(abbr.)*
46. British treasurer who started the Stamp Act
48. "Mother of Presidents" state *(abbr.)*

DOWN:

1. Virginia delegate to the Second Continental Congress
2. "Free religion" colony *(abbr.)*
3. South Carolina *(abbr.)*
4. Colony founded by Quakers *(abbr.)*
5. Helped organize the Sons of Liberty
6. British treasurer who taxed glass, paint, paper, etc.
7. Delaware *(abbr.)*
8. Maryland *(abbr.)*
9. "The British are coming"
11. British Prime Minister who passed the Intolerable Acts
13. British general who evacuated Boston
15. Author of "Common Sense"
17. Colonial leader and smuggler
20. Virginia delegate to the Second Continental Congress

21. Leader of the Green Mountain Boys
22. Virginia delegate to the Second Continental Congress
23. British statesman in favor of the colonists
26. Colonial patriot who warned of British attack
27. President of the Second Continental Congress
36. Massachusetts delegate to the Second Continental Congress
37. British philosopher
40. New Hampshire *(abbr.)*
41. New York *(abbr.)*
43. Colonial critic of King George III
46. Georgia *(abbr.)*
47. North Carolina *(abbr.)*

8. The Idea of Liberty

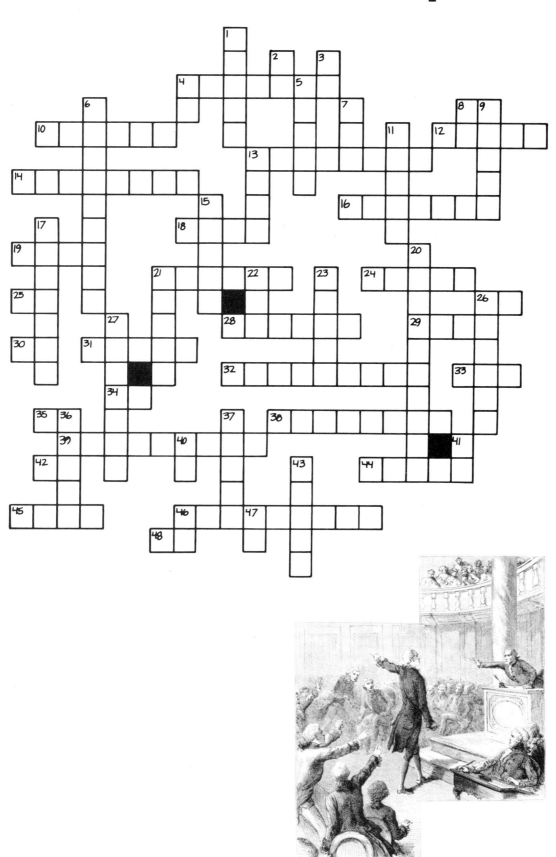

9. THE DECLARATION OF INDEPENDENCE

ACROSS:

2. British king
3. Co-author of the Declaration
6. Delegate from Rhode Island
8. Number of committee members to write the Declaration
12. Main author of the Declaration
16. Delegate from New Jersey
18. Unalienable right
20. City in which the Declaration was written
22. Number of Declaration authors
25. Delegate from Massachusetts
26. "All men are created _____."
28. Delegates who proposed independence
29. Home state of Roger Sherman *(abbr.)*
30. Month in which the Declaration was written
31. Delegate from Connecticut
32. Delegate from Virginia
36. Americans who favored independence
37. Home state of Samuel Adams *(abbr.)*
38. Home state of Richard Henry Lee *(abbr.)*
40. Delegate from Virginia
41. Date the Declaration was written
43. State where the Declaration was written *(abbr.)*
44. Delegate from Massachusetts
46. Home state of Benjamin Franklin *(abbr.)*
47. Delegate from Virginia
48. Americans who opposed independence
49. Author of "natural rights"
51. Co-author of the Declaration
53. Delegate from North Carolina
54. "We must all hang together, or most assuredly, we shall all hang separately"
55. Home state of John Adams *(abbr.)*

DOWN:

1. Delegate from North Carolina
4. The _____ Continental Congress wrote the Declaration
5. Delegate from Delaware
7. Delegate from New Jersey
9. Where the Declaration was written
10. Writer of the Declaration
11. "All _____ are created equal"
13. Delegate from Connecticut
14. Co-author of the Declaration
15. Unalienable right
17. "_____, liberty, and the pursuit of happiness"
19. Delegate from Pennsylvania
21. Co-author of the Declaration
23. Unalienable right
24. _____ 4, 1776
27. "These United Colonies are, and of a right ought to be, free and independent States"
30. Delegate from Virginia
32. "Life, _____, and the pursuit of happiness"
33. Home state of Thomas Jefferson *(abbr.)*
34. Introduction of the Declaration
35. King of England
39. "Life, liberty, and the pursuit of _____"
42. President of the Second Continental Congress
45. Delegate from Massachusetts
47. People excluded from "all men are created equal"
50. Home state of Benjamin Franklin *(abbr.)*
52. Home state of Robert Livingston *(abbr.)*

9. The Declaration of Independence

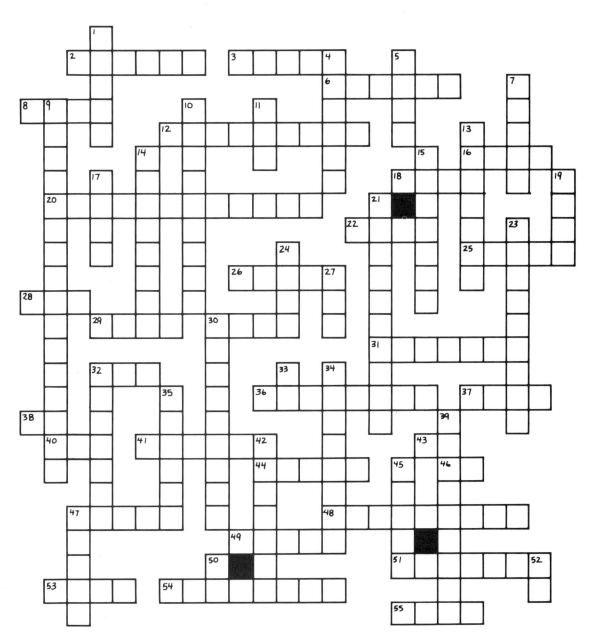

SIGNING THE DECLARATION OF INDEPENDENCE

10. THE AMERICAN REVOLUTIONARY WAR

ACROSS:

4. First battle of the Revolution
6. Negotiator at the Treaty of Paris
7. Home state of Benjamin Franklin *(abbr.)*
11. Last battle of the Revolution
13. British general at Saratoga
15. German mercenaries
18. American general at Oriskany
19. Location of the peace treaty
23. Mary Ludwig Hays
25. First American battle victory
27. "The Swamp Fox"
28. "The Crisis"
30. British Prime Minister
31. American general at Saratoga
32. American "navy"
33. Home state of John Jay *(abbr.)*
38. Negotiator at the Treaty of Paris
40. British general at Yorktown
41. Location of the battle of White Plains *(abbr.)*
45. "_____ Pitcher"
46. French officer at Yorktown

DOWN:

1. River crossed by General Washington
2. "The Swamp _____"
3. Received Florida by the Treaty of Paris
5. Location of the battle of Trenton *(abbr.)*
8. American traitor in the Revolution
9. British general at Brooklyn Heights
10. Ambassador to France
12. American general at Yorktown
14. Location of the battle of Princeton *(abbr.)*
16. Location of the battle of Germantown *(abbr.)*
17. American winter camp
19. "These are the times that try men's souls"
20. British soldier
21. American soldiers
22. American ally
24. Treaty of _____
26. British general who replaced General Howe
29. Superintendent of finance
34. Negotiator at the Treaty of Paris
35. Home of Lafayette
36. Location of the battle of Bunker Hill *(abbr.)*
37. Location of Valley Forge *(abbr.)*
39. British spy hanged during the Revolution
42. Location of the battle of Brooklyn Heights *(abbr.)*
43. Location of the battle of Yorktown *(abbr.)*
44. Home state of General Washington *(abbr.)*

10. The American Revolutionary War

11. MEN AND WOMEN OF THE AMERICAN REVOLUTION

ACROSS:

7. German mercenaries
8. First American to die in the Revolution
10. American general at the battle of Oriskany
11. American soldiers
12. Led a farmers' rebellion in Massachusetts
13. Helped author the Declaration of Independence
16. Hancock or Adams
18. Female revolutionary soldier
20. "Give me liberty or give me death"
21. Delegate who proposed independence
23. Americans opposing independence
26. Polish military aide
27. President of the Second Continental Congress
28. "The Swamp _____"
29. "_____ of Liberty"
30. "I have not yet begun to fight"
32. American military leader in the South
33. American general at the battle of Saratoga
36. John _____ Jones
37. British Prime Minister
39. Richard Henry _____
41. Leader of the "Green Mountain Boys"
43. Adams or Hancock
44. British general at the battle of Brooklyn Heights
46. Loyalist
47. Negotiator at the Treaty of Paris
48. "The British are coming"
50. American in favor of independence
52. British general at the battle of Yorktown
53. British general at the battle of Bunker Hill
54. Author of "Common Sense"
55. Ambassador of England
57. "The Swamp Fox"
58. King of England
59. "The British are coming"
60. American leader at the battle of Vincennes
61. American general at the battle of Yorktown
67. Financial officer of the Second Continental Congress
68. "Green Mountain _____"
71. Author of the Declaration of Independence
72. British Prime Minister
73. "The British are coming"
76. British philosopher who influenced American independence
78. "Give me liberty or give me death"
79. Female soldier
80. American general at the battle of Trenton

DOWN:

1. Aide to General Washington
2. British statesman favoring American independence
3. Author of "natural rights"
4. "Letter from a Farmer in Pennsylvania"
5. British general at the battle of Saratoga
6. British general at the battle of Oriskany
7. "Molly Pitcher"
9. British general _____ Leger
12. Prussian military aide
14. Negotiator at the Treaty of Paris
15. British Prime Minister
17. American leader at the battle of Oriskany
19. British general at the battle of Monmouth Courthouse
21. French military aide
22. Negotiator at the Treaty of Paris
24. French military aide
25. "_____ of Liberty"
31. "_____ Pitcher"
33. American general at the battle of King's Mountain
34. American "navy"
35. Delegate who proposed independence
38. American traitor during the Revolution
40. Polish military aide
41. British spy
42. American spy
45. American at Valley Forge
49. British soldiers
51. French military aide
53. British general at the beginning of the Revolution
56. Massachusetts brothers
62. American leader at the battle of King's Mountain
63. Baron _____ Steuben
64. American naval hero
65. _____ Franklin
66. British military brothers
69. _____ Paul Jones
70. "Molly Pitcher"
74. "The Swamp Fox"
75. Patriot
77. John or Samuel

Name _____   Date _____

11. Men and Women of the American Revolution

12. BATTLES OF THE AMERICAN REVOLUTION

ACROSS: ───────────────────────

8. "Bunker Hill in reverse"

DOWN: ─────────────────────────

1. Final surrender of British General Cornwallis
2. First American victory in the Revolution
3. Defeat of the British near Lake Ontario
4. Surrender of British General Burgoyne
5. Battle including "Molly Pitcher"
6. Battle with a mistaken name
7. American victory in South Carolina

12. Battles of the American Revolution

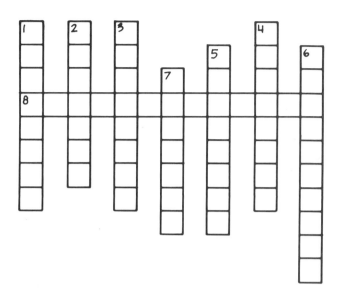

13. THE ARTICLES OF CONFEDERATION

ACROSS:

1. Virginia congressman
3. North _____ Ordinance
6. Home state of Benjamin Franklin *(abbr.)*
8. Home state of John Adams *(abbr.)*
10. British interest in Canada
14. Weakness of the Articles of Confederation *(two words)*
16. Power of the Articles of Confederation
18. Northern boundary of the Northwest Territory *(two words)*
19. Home state of Thomas Jefferson *(abbr.)*
20. One-house legislature
23. Virginia congressman
24. Home state of Samuel Adams *(abbr.)*
29. Southern boundary of the Northwest Territory

31. Led a farmers' rebellion in Massachusetts
32. Number of votes each state had in Congress
33. Location of Shays' Rebellion *(abbr.)*
35. State created from the Northwest Territory
36. State created from the Northwest Territory
37. State created from the Northwest Territory
38. Home state of Patrick Henry *(abbr.)*
39. Home state of John Jay *(abbr.)*
41. Only state with a one-house legislature
44. Author of the Northwest Ordinance

DOWN:

2. Massachusetts congressman
3. Power of the Articles of Confederation
4. New York congressman
5. One requirement of the Northwest Ordinance
7. Weakness of the Articles of Confederation
9. Right to vote
10. Pennsylvania congressman
11. Law for governing the western territory
12. Weakness of the Articles of Confederation
13. Two-house legislature
15. Power of the Articles of Confederation
17. _____ Rebellion
21. "What a triumph for our enemies . . . to find we are incapable of governing ourselves"

22. Western boundary of the Northwest Territory
25. Location of Shays' Rebellion *(abbr.)*
26. Number of states created from the Northwest Territory
27. Ambassador to Spain
28. State created from the Northwest Territory
30. State created from the Northwest Territory
34. Massachusetts congressman
38. Home state of James Madison *(abbr.)*
40. Number of votes each state had in Congress
42. Home state of Alexander Hamilton *(abbr.)*
43. Home state of George Washington *(abbr.)*

13. The Articles of Confederation

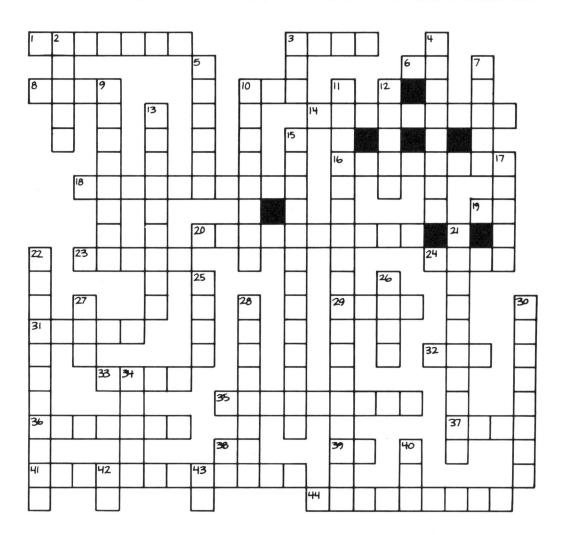

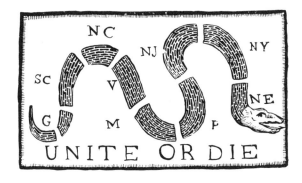

UNITE OR DIE

14. THE CONSTITUTION

ACROSS:

1. "Father of the Constitution"
4. Home state of William Paterson *(abbr.)*
6. Addition to the Constitution
8. Judicial branch
10. Virginia representative who refused to attend the Constitutional Convention
14. Executive branch
16. Only state not to attend the Constitutional Convention *(abbr.)*
17. "This generation will die away and give place to a race of Americans"
18. Author of the Virginia Plan
21. "We had better take a supreme government now, than a despot twenty years hence—for come he must"
24. Home state of John Jay *(abbr.)*
25. Location of the Constitutional Convention
27. Branch of government
29. Smallest state *(abbr.)*
33. Legislative body based on equality
36. Home state of George Washington *(abbr.)*
37. Maryland *(abbr.)*
38. Number of slaves counted for representation
43. Home state of James Madison *(abbr.)*

45. Chairman of the Constitutional Convention
48. Only state not to attend the Constitutional Convention
49. New Hampshire *(abbr.)*
50. The Virginia _____
51. Branch of government
53. North Carolina *(abbr.)*
54. Smallest legislative body
56. Powers kept by the state governments
58. The New Jersey _____
59. Powers of both the state and federal governments
63. People in favor of a strong national government
65. Number of branches of government
66. Legislative branch
71. Antifederalist
73. Proposed the Constitutional Convention
74. First state to ratify the Constitution *(abbr.)*
75. Massachusetts *(abbr.)*
76. To strike down a law
77. Highest court
78. Suffrage

DOWN:

1. Secretary of the Constitutional Convention
2. Home state of Alexander Hamilton *(abbr.)*
3. One half of Congress
5. Wrote "The Federalist Papers"
7. Number of branches in the federal government
9. South Carolina *(abbr.)*
11. Number of delegates at the Constitutional Convention
12. President's refusal of a bill
13. Number of states needed to approve the Constitution
15. Number of senators from each state
17. New York delegate to the Constitutional Convention
19. "All other persons"
20. New York *(abbr.)*
22. Two-house legislature
23. Antifederalist
25. Pennsylvania *(abbr.)*
26. People opposed to a strong national government
27. "Publius"
28. Branch of government
30. Home state of Benjamin Franklin *(abbr.)*
31. Chairman of the Constitutional Convention

32. Presidential power
34. Home state of Alexander Hamilton *(abbr.)*
35. To accuse a politician of wrong doing
39. "Publius"
40. Proposed the Virginia Plan
41. First executive
42. Powers given to the federal government
44. Legislative body based on population
46. "The people, sir, are a great beast"
47. Home state of John Jay *(abbr.)*
52. The president's branch of government
55. Antifederalist
57. Last original state to ratify the Constitution *(abbr.)*
60. Smallest state *(abbr.)*
61. One half of Congress
62. Branch of government
64. _____ Court
67. Suffrage
68. Number of states needed to ratify the Constitution
69. Number of state votes under the New Jersey Plan
70. Number of senators from each state
72. Southern-most original state *(abbr.)*

Name _____   Date _____

14. The Constitution

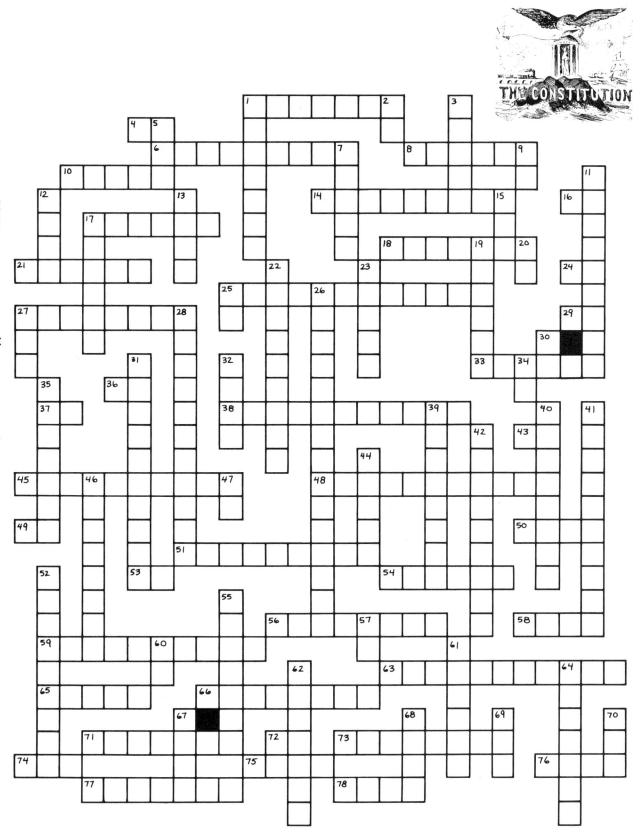

15. THE LEGISLATIVE BRANCH

ACROSS:

2. Bill that is dropped if congress adjourns *(two words)*
8. Major crime
11. Taxes on goods made in the United States
13. Printing false information about a person
14. Smallest number of representatives allowed
15. process of becoming an American citizen
17. Chairman of the Senate
23. Items that cannot be taxed by congress
24. Number of times congress must meet each year
25. President _____ Tempore
26. Congressional body based on population
27. Residence requirement for U.S. representatives and senators
29. Number of days required for a pocket veto
30. Powers kept by the state governments
31. Chairman of the House of Representatives
32. Opposite of aye
33. Proposed law
37. Years of citizenship required for a U.S. senator
40. Age required for a U.S. representative
41. Number of senators from each state
42. Bill passed over a president's veto
43. British philosopher who influenced American government
45. Taxes on goods coming into the United States
47. Number of U.S. senators for each state
48. Congressional body based on equality
50. Month of inauguration for U.S. senators and representatives
52. Protection from arrest for slander in congress
53. Function of the legislative branch *(two words)*
56. Years of term for a U.S. senator
57. Negative vote
58. Sole power of the House of Representatives
60. Years between the taking of a U.S. census
62. Years in three terms for a U.S. representative
63. Trade within one state
65. Powers of both the state and federal governments
66. Count of the population
67. Protection of an inventor's idea
71. Ex _____ facto law
75. Pass a law despite a veto by the President
76. Punishment without a trial *(three words)*
78. Total number of U.S. senators
79. Years of citizenship required for a U.S. representative
80. Common name for the legislative branch

DOWN:

1. Publication of the legislative branch *(two words)*
3. Election day
4. The final clause in Section 8 is called "_____"
5. Years of citizenship required for a U.S. representative
6. Years of age required for a U.S. senator
7. Protection of an author's idea
9. Jury in a trial of impeachment
10. President's refusal to sign a bill of congress
12. Making imitation money or stamps
16. Election month
18. National capital *(three words)*
19. Legislative body that must originate tax bills
20. Only president to have been impeached
21. Temporary chairman of the Senate
22. Protection from being jailed without evidence *(two words)*
28. Saying false statements about a person
32. Years of citizenship required for a U.S. senator
34. Trade between two or more states
35. Powers given to the federal government
36. Two-house legislature
38. _____ post facto law
39. Years of term for a U.S. senator
44. Majority of congressmen required for a session
46. Basis for the number of a state's representatives
49. Tax on imports
51. Positive vote
53. Ancestor of the National Guard
54. Proposed law
55. Ex post _____ law
59. Punishment for an act before it was illegal *(three words)*
61. Rejection of a bill by the President
64. Chief _____
68. Years of term for a U.S. representative
69. Number of votes for each U.S. senator
70. _____ Justice
72. Chairman of the House of Representatives
73. Referred to by the Three-Fifths Clause
74. Negative vote
77. Ex _____ facto law

© 1993 by The Center for Applied Research in Education

15. The Legislative Branch

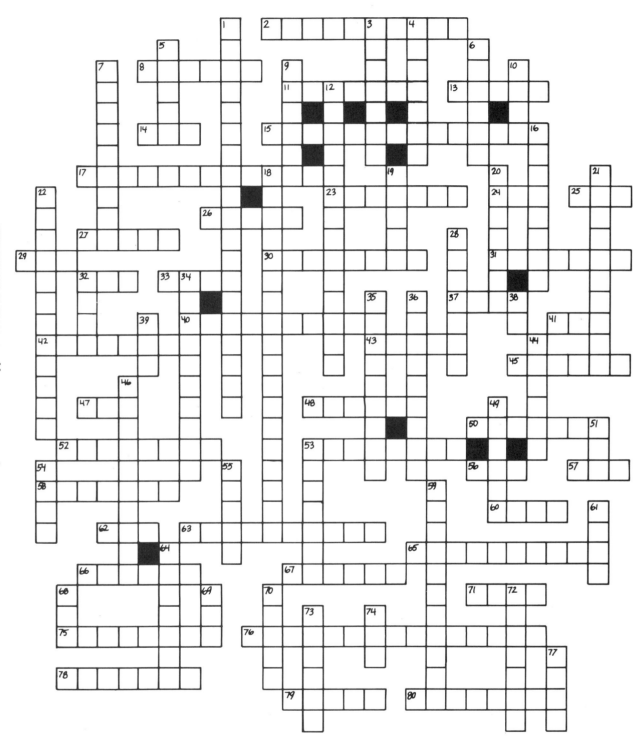

16. THE EXECUTIVE BRANCH

ACROSS:

2. Number of terms a president may be elected
6. Years of term for a president
9. Accusing the president of a crime
13. Grant a military rank
15. President's jury in a trial of impeachment
16. Number of presidents who have resigned from office
17. Years of age required to be president
21. Congressional body that can impeach the president
22. Number of presidents who have been assassinated
24. Years of residency required to be president
25. President's refusal to sign a bill of Congress into law

26. Becomes president if the president dies or resigns
30. Number of presidents to serve more than two terms
31. President's annual speech to the Congress *(five words)*
32. Only president to have been impeached
40. President's rejection of a bill of Congress
41. President's duty *(two words)*
43. Total number of years a president may serve
45. Number of terms a president may serve
46. U.S. representative in a foreign country
49. Chairman of the Senate
50. Congressional body that must approve president's cabinet
51. Number of presidents to be impeached

DOWN:

1. Father and son presidents
3. Residence of the president *(two words)*
4. Congressional body that must approve president's treaties
5. Number of presidents to resign from office
7. State of the _____ Message
8. Head of the executive branch
10. Presidential advisors
11. Number of presidents to be impeached
12. First executive
14. Number of presidents to serve more than one term
18. Number of terms a president may serve
19. _____ president
20. Election day
23. Only president to resign from office
25. President's refusal to sign a bill into law
27. Election month

28. Years in a president's term
29. Number of presidents to serve two separate terms
33. The president must take an _____ of office
34. Congressional body that must approve president's judge selections
35. Congressional body that must approve president's ambassador selections
36. Statutes enacted by the legislative body
37. Presidential power to release criminals from punishment
38. _____ House
39. Inauguration month *(abbr.)*
42. _____ of the Union Message
44. Times a president may be elected
47. United States of America *(abbr.)*
48. Only president to serve four terms *(abbr.)*

16. The Executive Branch

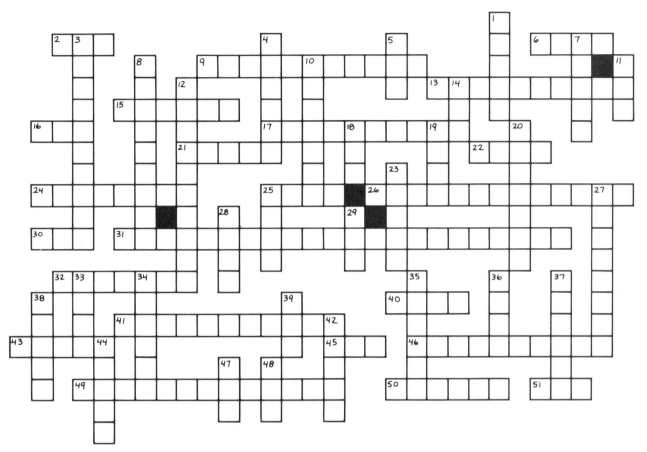

17. THE JUDICIAL BRANCH

ACROSS:

1. First woman justice of the Supreme Court
5. Lying in court
9. Body of citizens that judges an individual
11. Temporary release from jail
12. Officer of the court
13. An excuse for not committing a crime
15. War against your own country
16. Number of justices on the Supreme Court
17. Not consistent with the Constitution
18. Person who commits treason
19. Judges
24. Number of justices on the Supreme Court

27. Highest court in the United States *(two words)*
28. Home state of Chief Justice John Jay *(abbr.)*
30. To accuse a judge of a crime
32. Attorney
34. Giving aid to the enemy
35. Number of citizens on a criminal jury
37. The judicial branch is to interpret _____
39. To return a fugitive to the state of the crime
41. A schedule of court cases
45. Serious crime punishable by at least a year in prison
46. _____ Court
47. First Chief Justice of the Supreme Court

DOWN:

2. Head judge of the Supreme Court *(two words)*
3. The authority to interpret the law
4. The limits of the court's authority
6. To retry a case in a higher court
7. A person who testifies against you
8. A statement of having been elsewhere at the time of the crime
9. Power to decide if a law violates the Constitution *(two words)*
10. Term of office for a Supreme Court judge
14. Bond
20. Disrespect in court
21. Minor crime punishable by fine or short prison term
22. To ask for another trial
23. Lawyer

25. Money paid for release from jail until the trial
26. To admit to a crime
29. Bond
31. Required location of a trial
33. The Supreme Court is comprised of _____ Chief Justice and eight Associate Justices.
34. A case presented in court
36. A person who testifies for you
38. Term of office for Supreme Court judges
40. A court case
42. Number of witnesses needed to convict for treason
43. Number of African-Americans on the Supreme Court as of 1993
44. To take a person to court

17. The Judicial Branch

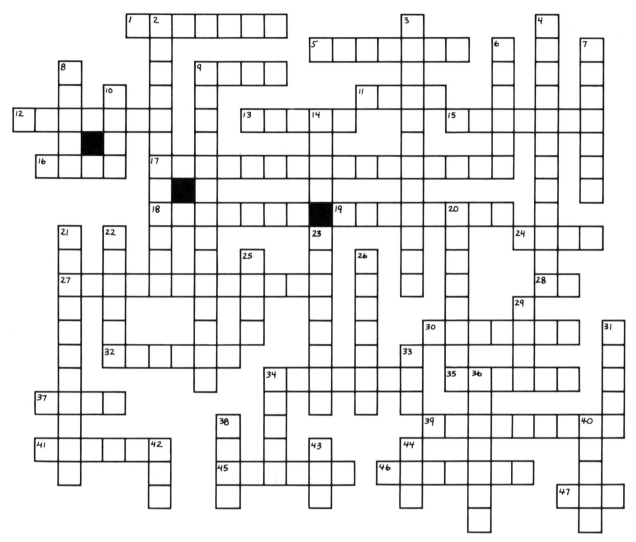

18. THE BILL OF RIGHTS

ACROSS:

1. Right of the eighth amendment
7. To testify against one's self *(two words)*
13. Government taking private property for public use *(two words)*
14. Money to guarantee appearance in court
15. Right of the second amendment *(two words)*
16. Bail
17. Required location of a trial
19. One who authorizes a legal search warrant
21. Number of amendments in the Bill of Rights
23. A legal document to search
24. Powers of both state and federal governments
29. Author of the Bill of Rights
30. Right of the first amendment
32. Right of the first amendment
34. Right of the first amendment
35. Attorney
37. Proper and orderly working of the legal system *(two words)*

DOWN:

2. Right of the first amendment
3. Powers given to the federal government
4. Person testifying for or against you
5. Crime punishable by imprisonment
6. Being tried twice for the same crime *(two words)*
8. One who refuses military service on the basis of religion *(two words)*
9. Accusation of a major crime
10. Number of amendments in the Bill of Rights
11. Military force made up of civilians
12. Group that determines whether to accuse someone of a crime *(two words)*
18. Right of the sixth amendment
20. Rights protected by the Constitution *(two words)*
22. Addition to the Constitution
24. Unwritten law
25. Crime punishable by death
26. Written law
27. Powers kept by the state governments
28. The Bill of Rights are the first _____ amendments
31. Rights of the first amendment
33. _____ jury
36. Month the Bill of Rights was added to the Constitution *(abbr.)*

18. The Bill of Rights

OUR RIGHTS AND OUR LIBERTIES.

L. JOHNSON & Co.

19. AMENDMENTS TO THE CONSTITUTION

ACROSS:

4. Voting age before the twenty-sixth amendment
6. Suffrage
7. Month of inauguration for congressmen and congresswomen *(abbr.)*
8. Twentieth amendment *(two words)*
10. Limit of presidential terms
12. One of two presidents chosen by the House of Representatives
13. Years in a senator's term
14. Amendment that abolished the quartering of troops
16. Years in a president's term
19. Number of votes for each senator
22. Only president to serve more than two terms
23. Leader for women's suffrage
26. Amendment that grants freedom of speech and press
27. One of two presidents chosen by the House of Representatives
28. "_____ duck"
30. Time that Congress meets
33. Author of the Bill of Rights
34. Number of presidents who have resigned
35. Thirteenth amendment

DOWN:

1. Amendment that abolished the poll tax
2. Stopped by the twenty-fourth amendment *(two words)*
3. Amendment that reserved powers for the states
5. Only president to resign
6. Successor if the president is disabled
7. Month the president is inaugurated *(abbr.)*
9. National capital *(three words)*
11. Eighteenth amendment
13. Amendment that created income tax
15. Age required to vote
17. President who pardoned Richard Nixon
18. Abolished by the thirteenth amendment
20. Amendment that abolished slavery
21. Amendment that gave women the right to vote
24. _____ of Representatives
25. Civil _____
29. President who signed the twenty-sixth amendment
31. President chosen by the House of Representatives
32. _____ rights

19. Amendments to the Constitution

JAMES MADISON.

20. OUR FOUNDING FATHERS

ACROSS:

5. "Father of the Constitution"
8. "All men are created equal"
10. First Chief Justice of the Supreme Court
12. First Secretary of State
14. First president
15. First Chief Justice
17. Massachusetts delegate to the Second Continental Congress
19. "I shall sign so boldly the king shall read it without his glasses"
21. New York delegate to the Constitutional Convention
22. New Jersey delegate to the Second Continental Congress
23. Proposed the Virginia Plan of representation
26. New York delegate who helped write the Declaration of Independence
28. Connecticut delegate who helped write the Declaration of Independence
29. Massachusetts delegate to the Constitutional Convention
31. Proposed the New Jersey Plan of representation
33. Georgia delegate to the Second Continental Congress
35. Pennsylvania delegate to the Second Continental Congress
36. Delaware delegate to the Second Continental Congress
38. Author of the Declaration of Independence
39. New Jersey delegate to the Second Continental Congress
40. North Carolina delegate to the Second Continental Congress
41. Pennsylvania delegate to the Second Continental Congress

DOWN:

1. Chairman of the Constitutional Convention
2. Chairman of the Second Constitutional Congress
3. Pennsylvania delegate to the Second Continental Congress
4. Virginia delegate who proposed American independence
6. Connecticut delegate to the Constitutional Convention
7. First Secretary of War
9. "We must all hang together or, most assuredly, we shall all hang separately"
11. Massachusetts delegate who helped write the Declaration of Independence
13. Georgia delegate to the Constitutional Convention
16. Pennsylvania delegate who helped write the Declaration of Independence
18. First attorney general
20. First vice-president
22. Proposed the Constitutional Convention
24. Chairman of the Second Continental Convention
25. Secretary of the Constitution Convention
27. Author of the Great Compromise
30. New York delegate to the Second Continental Congress
32. Pennsylvania delegate to the Second Continental Congress
34. Virginia delegate to the Second Continental Congress
35. Pennsylvania delegate to the Second Continental Congress
37. Maryland delegate to the Second Continental Congress

20. Our Founding Fathers

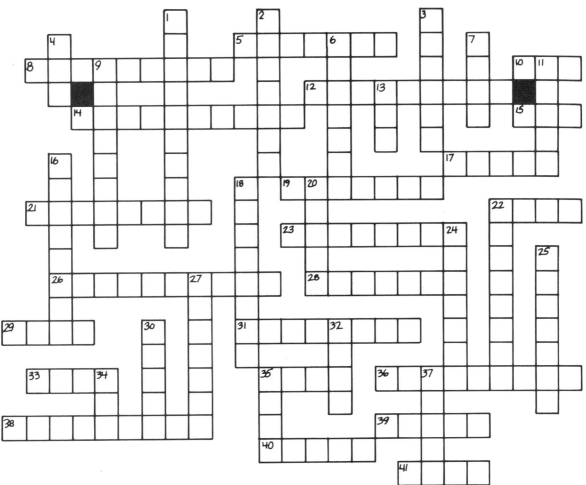

21. THE FIRST PRESIDENCY

ACROSS:

2. Number of terms for George Washington
6. Number of amendments in the Bill of Rights
7. Home state of John Adams *(abbr.)*
10. President's advisors
12. Political party of Thomas Jefferson
13. Washington's wife
14. Tax on American-made goods
15. _____ of Rights
16. Number of Supreme Court judges in 1789
17. Smallest state *(abbr.)*
18. First Secretary of State
24. Cabinet member's title
27. Washington's foreign policy
28. Number of amendments in the Bill of Rights
29. Washington's home *(two words)*
31. Country for Jay's Treaty
33. Tax that caused the Whiskey Rebellion
35. Treaty to gain the Northwest Territory
37. City of the First Bank of the United States

39. _____ York
41. Caused rebellion in Pennsylvania
42. Kidnapping of American sailors
45. Judiciary _____ of 1789
46. Home state of George Washington *(abbr.)*
48. Made a treaty with England
49. River by the U.S. capitol
52. North Carolina *(abbr.)*
53. Made a treaty with Spain
54. Number of Chief Justices on the Supreme Court
55. Location of Washington's inauguration *(abbr.)*
56. State that donated land for the District of Columbia *(abbr.)*
57. Number of associate judges on the Supreme Court in 1789
58. _____ Indies
59. Country for Pinckney's Treaty
60. King of France

DOWN:

1. Leader who put down the Whiskey Rebellion
2. Tax on foreign imports
3. First state to ratify the Constitution *(abbr.)*
4. First president
5. First Secretary of War
8. _____ Federalists
9. First Secretary of the Treasury
11. Started the Bank of the United States
18. First Chief Justice of the Supreme Court
19. Political party of Alexander Hamilton
20. Home state of Alexander Hamilton *(abbr.)*
21. Architect of Washington, D.C.
22. National capital *(abbr.)*
23. Leader of the Republican Party
25. First attorney general
26. Home state of Henry Knox *(abbr.)*

28. Excise _____
30. Home state of Thomas Jefferson *(abbr.)*
32. New Hampshire *(abbr.)*
34. First vice-president
35. French Ambassador
36. Home state of Edmund Randolph *(abbr.)*
38. First Postmaster General
40. General at the Battle of Fallen Timbers
41. "Mad Anthony"
43. "_____ Anthony" Wayne
44. Home state of Andrew Jackson
46. Home state of George Washington *(abbr.)*
47. Virginia *(abbr.)*
48. First Chief Justice
50. Home state of John Adams *(abbr.)*
51. Location of the Whiskey Rebellion *(abbr.)*
53. Pennsylvania *(abbr.)*
59. South Carolina *(abbr.)*

Name _____ Date _____

21. The First Presidency

22. THE FIRST CABINET

ACROSS: _____

4. Secretary of the Treasury
5. Postmaster General

DOWN: _____

1. Secretary of State
2. Secretary of War
3. Attorney General

Name _____ Date _____

23. THE LOUISIANA PURCHASE

ACROS: _____

2. River in the Louisiana Territory
4. "Long _____" Jefferson
7. King for which Louisiana was named
8. Ambassador to purchase Louisiana
10. Ambassador to purchase Louisiana
11. River in the Louisiana Territory
14. Price of Louisiana (in millions)
18. French emperor who sold Louisiana to the United States
19. Louisiana (abbr.)
21. Country that sold Louisiana to the United States
23. River in the Louisiana Territory
25. Jefferson's inauguration location (abbr.)
26. Name for the Louisiana Territory today (two words)
28. New _____
29. Northern border of the Louisiana Territory
33. River in the Louisiana Territory
34. President who purchased Louisiana
36. National capital (abbr.)
37. River in the Louisiana Territory (abbr.)
38. Original residents of the Louisiana Territory
39. Home of Napoleon

DOWN: _____

1. Lewis and Clark's expedition took over _____ years
3. Indian tribe of Sacajawea
5. Eastern boundary of the Louisiana Territory
6. Western boundary of the Louisiana Territory
7. Louisiana explorer
9. Slave of William Clark
12. Port at the mouth of the Mississippi River
13. Home of LaSalle
15. French foreign minister
16. United States president
17. Louisiana explorer
19. French explorer who named the Louisiana Territory
20. Namesake of the Louisiana Territory
22. Indian guide of Lewis and Clark
24. River in the Louisiana Territory
27. Emperor of France
30. River in the Louisiana Territory
31. Capital of France
32. River in the Louisiana Territory
35. River in the Louisiana Territory

24. THE WAR OF 1812

ACROSS:

6. A strong pride in one's country
8. National song
11. North Carolina *(abbr.)*
14. "We have met the enemy and they are ours"
15. Indian tribe of Tecumseh
17. Location of the Tippecanoe River
19. Emperor of France
21. War hawk from Kentucky
22. Nickname of the USS Constitution
25. One who does not believe in war
27. Home state of President Madison *(abbr.)*
29. Month the War of 1812 was declared
30. Home state of Henry Clay *(abbr.)*
31. Home state of James Monroe *(abbr.)*
32. Home state of Andrew Jackson *(abbr.)*
33. Battle of the War of 1812
36. Author of the national anthem
37. Great Lake where Commodore Perry fought
38. War hawk from South Carolina
39. United States' war ship
41. Home state of John Quincy Adams *(abbr.)*
44. Chief of the Shawnee Indians
45. Home state of John C. Calhoun *(abbr.)*
46. State bordering Washington, D.C. *(abbr.)*
48. Wife of President Madison
53. American general in the War of 1812
55. President who succeeded James Madison
56. Chief of the Seminole Indians
58. Home state of Andrew Jackson *(abbr.)*
60. Birthplace of Andrew Jackson *(abbr.)*
61. Author of the *Star Spangled Banner*
64. One who does not fear war
66. American naval leader in the War of 1812
68. British foreign minister
69. Great Lake
71. "_____ hawk"
72. Home state of Henry Clay *(abbr.)*
73. Battle of Put-in-_____
75. Month the war started
78. _____ *Spangled Banner*
79. Opposite of a "hawk"
80. American ship
81. Present location of Fort Dearborn
83. Location of the Battle of Pensacola *(abbr.)*
84. New York *(abbr.)*
85. Location of Fort McHenry
87. _____ Orleans
88. New _____
89. Georgia *(abbr.)*
90. What was present-day Toronto
91. "Mr. _____ War"
92. Opponent in the War of 1812

DOWN:

1. City burned by the British in the War of 1812
2. Battle where Napoleon was defeated
3. River where Shawnee Indians lived
4. Famous American painter
5. United States fort massacred by Indians
7. United States president during the War of 1812
9. Tenskwatawa
10. New York *(abbr.)*
12. Location of the Hartford Convention *(abbr.)*
13. Fort where the national anthem was written
16. "Dove" from New Hampshire
18. Monroe _____
20. Location of New Orleans *(abbr.)*
23. Kidnapping of American sailors
24. Battle that occurred after the peace agreement
25. Battle in the War of 1812
26. Location of Oliver H. Perry
28. American Secretary of State
29. War of 1812 hero
34. French leader
35. Ambassador from Spain
40. Fort Dearborn
41. Location of Fort McHenry *(abbr.)*
42. Battle of _____-in-Bay
43. New England spokesman
47. United States war ship
49. Battle of the War of 1812
50. United States war ship
51. Indians of Florida
52. Battle in the War of 1812
54. Rhode Island *(abbr.)*
57. Leaving the Union of the United States
59. Country for the Adams-Onis Treaty
62. American military leader at the Battle of New Orleans
63. _____ York
65. Home state of Henry Clay *(abbr.)*
67. Convention to separate New England from the United States
70. Location of the Battle of Lundy's Lane *(abbr.)*
74. Location of the peace agreement
76. Hemisphere protected by the Monroe Doctrine
77. Home state of James Madison *(abbr.)*
81. Land owned by the British in the War of 1812
82. *Star Spangled* _____
85. Battle of Horseshoe _____
86. Home state of John Quincy Adams *(abbr.)*
88. "_____ Hickory"

24. The War of 1812

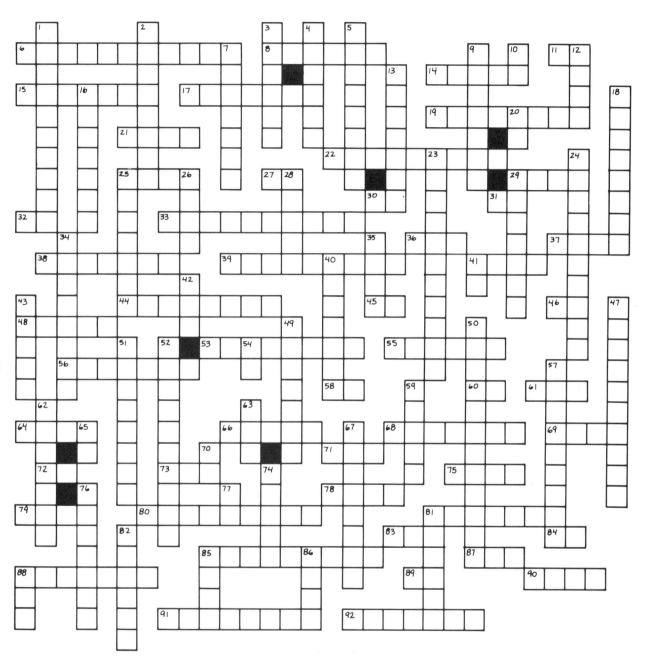

25. THE ERA OF GOOD FEELINGS

ACROSS:

3. Cash crop of the southern states
4. High tariff to limit foreign competition
7. Cash crop of the southern states
8. Free state added to the Union by the Missouri Compromise
13. State where the Natchez Trace began *(abbr.)*
15. Cash crop of the southern states
16. Road built through the Cumberland Gap
18. Home state of John Quincy Adams *(abbr.)*
20. Principles warning Europe not to interfere in the Western Hemisphere *(two words)*
21. Crop of South Carolina
22. Home state of President Monroe *(abbr.)*

23. Canal joining Lake Erie and the Hudson River
25. Inventor of the cotton gin
26. Chief Justice of the Supreme Court
28. Author of the Missouri Compromise
29. State added to the Union in 1817 *(abbr.)*
31. Home state of Eli Whitney *(abbr.)*
32. _____ Canal
33. State added to the Union in 1819 *(abbr.)*
36. Location of the Wilderness Road *(abbr.)*
37. Home state of Henry Clay
39. State added to the Union in 1816
41. Home state of James Monroe
42. Author of the American System

DOWN:

1. Cash crop of the southern states
2. Crop of Louisiana
3. Political party of President James Monroe
5. President Monroe's Secretary of State
6. Industrial area of the United States
9. Road heading west from Baltimore
10. Home state of John Marshall
11. State added to the Union in 1821
12. President during the Era of Good Feelings
14. Road heading south from Nashville
17. Agricultural area of the United States

19. Treaty that added Florida to the United States
24. State added to the Union in 1818
25. Inventor of interchangeable parts
27. Founder of the colony of Texas
28. "The Great Compromiser"
30. _____ Carolina
34. Location of the Cumberland Gap *(abbr.)*
35. Indiana *(abbr.)*
38. Kentucky *(abbr.)*
39. Illinois *(abbr.)*
40. Virginia *(abbr.)*

Name _____ Date _____

25. The Era of Good Feelings

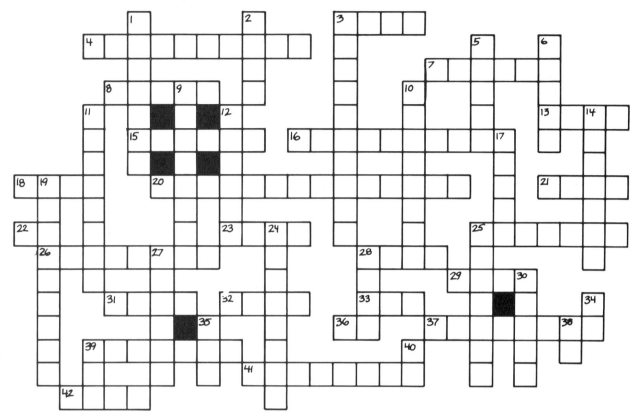

26. THE JACKSONIAN PERIOD

ACROSS:

2. Jackson's Chief Justice of the Supreme Court
4. Jackson's favorite state banks
10. Jackson's Secretary of State
12. Chief of the Seminole Indians
13. Jackson's vice-president
14. Location of the Chocktaw Indians (abbr.)
15. Indian Territory
18. Act that moved the Indians to the West
20. Location of the Cherokee Indians (abbr.)
21. Home state of John C. Calhoun (abbr.)
22. "_____ Hickory"
23. Indians led by Chief Black Hawk
26. Tax on foreign imports
28. Republican candidate in the 1832 election
29. Political opponent of President Jackson
30. Jackson's unofficial advisors (two words)
33. "Yankee Tariff of Abomination"

35. Location of the Cherokee Indians (abbr.)
36. Home of Andrew Jackson
40. Home state of Henry Clay (abbr.)
41. Location of the Seminole Indians (abbr.)
45. Birthplace of President Jackson (abbr.)
46. "_____ Hickory"
47. Battle where Jackson became a war hero
49. Seminole chief
50. First president since George Washington without a college education
56. Chief of the Sac and the Fox Indians (two words)
57. President of the National Bank
58. Home state of Martin Van Buren (abbr.)
59. Bill that authorized the use of federal troops against a state
60. Location of Wall Street (abbr.)

DOWN:

1. Street of U.S. financial institutions
3. Replacing old presidential appointees with new friends (two words)
5. Movement of the Cherokee Indians to Oklahoma (three words)
6. The Black _____ War
7. Location of the Seminole Indians (abbr.)
8. Nickname of President Jackson (two words)
9. Political party of President Jackson
11. Indians of Georgia
15. Another nickname of President Jackson (two words)
16. Absorbing the Indians into American culture
17. Location of the Creek Indians (abbr.)
19. "Liberty and Union, now and forever, one and inseparable!"
24. Political opponent of President Jackson
25. Indians of Mississippi
27. Indians of Florida

30. Another nickname of President Jackson (two words)
31. Number of terms for President Jackson
32. "The Union, next to our liberty, most dear"
34. Chief Black _____
36. "Old _____"
37. Indians of Alabama
38. "Our Union: it must be preserved"
39. Leader of the Bank of the United States
42. First president from west of the Appalachian Mountains
43. Indians of Illinois
44. Home state of President Jackson (abbr.)
48. Home state of Henry Clay (abbr.)
51. "The Great Compromiser"
52. Indians of Illinois
53. Number of terms for President Jackson
54. Location of the Seminole Indians (abbr.)
55. Birthplace of President Jackson (abbr.)

Name _____ Date _____

26. The Jacksonian Period

27. INVENTORS AND REFORMERS

ACROSS: _____

4. Antislavery spokeswoman
9. Mechanical reaper
11. American Antislavery Society
12. First woman's college
13. Antislavery spokeswoman
17. "Underground railroad"
19. American Colonization Society
20. First high school for girls
21. "Bloomers"
22. School to train black women teachers
24. Help for the mentally ill
26. Steamboat
28. Normal school
29. World's Antislavery Convention

30. Steam engine
33. Steel plow
34. Cotton gin
36. *The Lily*
37. Financer of Samuel Slater
39. Improved the sewing machine
41. *Blue Back Spellers*
44. Vulcanized rubber
45. Cast-iron plow
47. "Father of the American Factory System"
48. Monrovia, Liberia
49. Dictionary
50. St. Elizabeth's Hospital

DOWN: _____

1. "Bloomers" designer
2. Telegraph
3. St. Elizabeth's Hospital
5. World's Antislavery Convention
6. Slave rebellion in Virginia
7. *The Liberator*
8. Printing press
10. Shipping blacks back to Africa
13. "What Hath God Wrought"
14. "The Moses of her people"
15. Printing press
16. First woman doctor
18. First school to train teachers
19. Repeating pistol
20. Interchangeable parts

23. *The Clermont*
25. Murdered abolitionist
27. Steam engine
29. First full-time factory in America
31. Mount Holyoke Female Seminary
32. *The North Star*
35. Sewing machine
37. Financer of Samuel Slater
38. Telephone
40. "Watson, come in here"
41. Steam engine
42. First college for training teachers
43. Sewing machine
46. Public hospitals for the insane

27. Inventors and Reformers

28. THE MEXICAN WAR

© 1993 by The Center for Applied Research in Education

ACROSS:

3. The Bear Flag state
6. "The Long Marcher"
9. Mexican claimed border with Texas
11. Defender of the Alamo
12. American president during the Mexican War
13. Bear _____ state
14. Battle of the Mexican War
16. English-speaking whites
19. American general
21. Treaty to end the Mexican War *(two words)*
24. American general
26. Treaty of _____ Hidalgo
27. _____ Flag state
28. The Lone Star state
29. American general
32. American general
33. "Old Fuss and Feathers"
36. First amphibious battle
37. Capital of Texas
39. First battle of the Mexican War
40. The Volunteer state *(abbr.)*
41. Battle of the Mexican War
42. _____ Grande
43. _____ Anna

DOWN:

1. Nickname of California *(two words)*
2. President of Mexico
4. _____ Star state
5. Founder of Texas
7. California symbol
8. The Volunteer state
10. Defender of the Alamo
15. President of the Lone Star Republic
17. Boundary between Texas and Mexico
18. Vice-president of the Lone Star Republic
19. American leader at the battle of Buena Vista
20. Texas state nickname *(two words)*
22. Survivor of the Alamo
23. The Lone Star Republic
25. American general
30. Purchased land from Mexico in 1853
31. American general
34. "Old Rough and Ready"
35. Founder of Texas
38. Santa _____

28. The Mexican War

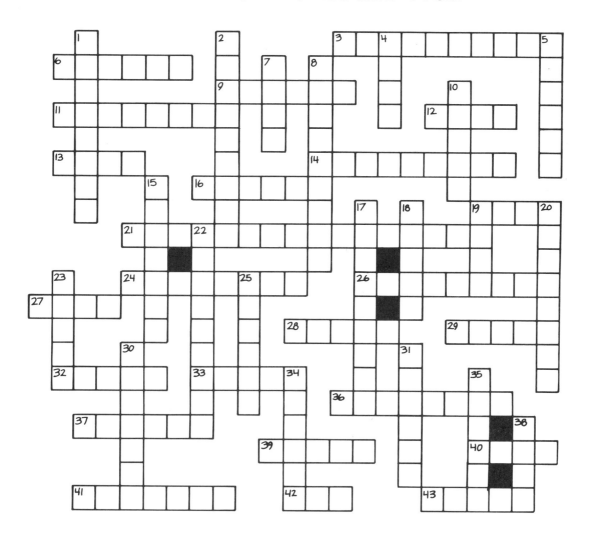

29. MANIFEST DESTINY

ACROSS:

5. Home state of John C. Calhoun *(abbr.)*
8. American ambassador to Mexico
9. The Bear _____ state
11. Home state of President Harrison
12. President Tyler's Secretary of State
13. Vice-president of William Henry Harrison
14. Religion of most Mexicans
16. Symbol of California
17. "Fifty-four, forty or _____"
19. Author of *Civil Disobedience*
20. A trip on the Santa Fe Trail took _____ weeks
21. Discovered gold in California
23. Spanish forts
26. Explorer of the West
28. Trail to the Southwest
32. Home state of Sam Houston *(abbr.)*
33. Naval leader who captured Monterey
34. Number of terms for President Van Buren
35. Wagon train killed, with few survivors, in the Rockies
36. President when Texas became a republic
37. Texas was a republic for nine _____
39. _____ Carson
41. American general in the Mexican War
44. Survivor of the Alamo
45. Led the first wagon train to Texas
46. The Lone Star Republic
48. Home state of Andrew Jackson *(abbr.)*
50. _____ Grande River
52. Indians of the West
55. "Tippecanoe and Tyler, too"
57. _____ Crockett
58. Indians of the West
59. "Fifty _____, forty or fight"
61. Scout for John C. Fremont
62. Led the first wagon train across the Rockies
63. "Old _____ and Ready"
65. President during the Mexican War
66. English-speaking whites
69. Number of terms for President Harrison
71. Illinois congressman
72. Boundary between the United States and Mexico
77. Explorer of the West
79. First vice-president to succeed to the presidency
82. President of the Republic of Texas
84. Inventor of the repeating pistol
85. Home state of Henry Clay *(abbr.)*
86. Leader of Mexico
87. Nickname of Tennessee

DOWN:

1. _____ Carson
2. "Remember the _____"
3. Author of "popular sovereignty"
4. British prime minister
6. Nickname of the Rocky Mountains *(two words)*
7. Symbol of Texas *(two words)*
10. _____ Star Republic
12. First woman to travel west
15. American commander of the Alamo
17. "Old _____ and Feathers"
18. President when Texas became a state
22. Religion of most Anglos
24. Owner of land where gold was discovered in California
25. Santa _____
27. Home state of Henry Clay *(abbr.)*
29. Home state of Davy Crockett *(abbr.)*
30. General in the Mexican War
31. Whig candidate in the 1844 election
38. British ambassador in the United States
40. Number of years Texas was a republic
42. Inventor of the repeating pistol
43. Home state of President Polk *(abbr.)*
47. Congressman against slavery
49. Missouri senator
51. Home state of President Tyler *(abbr.)*
53. Indians of the West
54. Led the first wagon train to California
56. Defender of the Alamo
59. "Fifty _____, forty or fight"
60. "Old Rough and Ready"
61. President Tyler's Secretary of State
64. "Tippecanoe and _____, too"
65. Home state of David Wilmot *(abbr.)*
67. Inventor of the telegraph
68. Missouri senator
70. "Go west, young man, go west"
73. Capital of Texas
74. "Father of Texas"
75. Home state of President Van Buren *(abbr.)*
76. Defender of the Alamo
78. Home state of President Lincoln *(abbr.)*
80. _____ Grande River
81. _____ Carson
83. Home state of President Tyler *(abbr.)*

29. Manifest Destiny

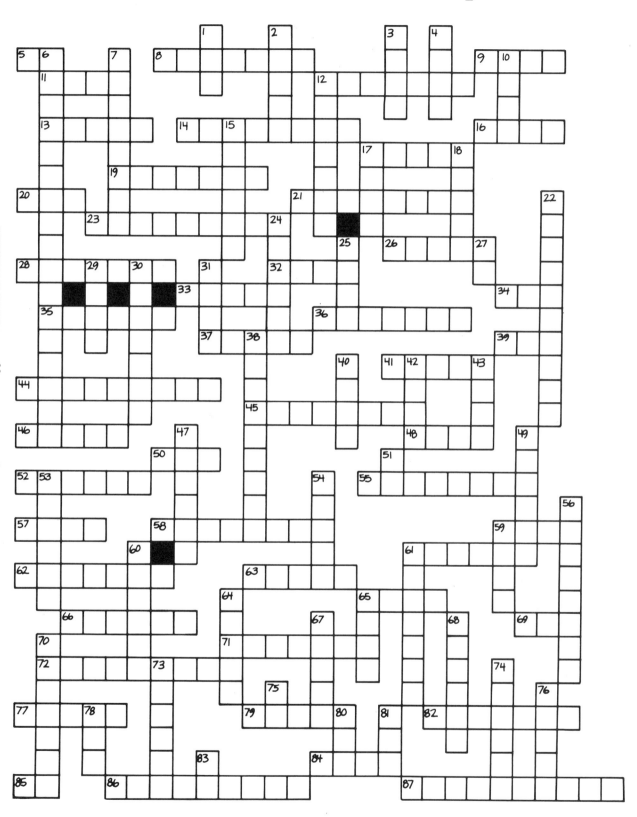

30. THE CIVIL WAR

ACROSS: _____

2. First battle of the Civil War *(two words)*
3. Union ironclad ship
4. Confederate ironclad ship
5. Site of the Confederate surrender
6. The draft
7. Confederate prisoner-of-war camp
8. Theater of Lincoln's assassination
9. Confederate capital
10. Beginning of Sherman's "march to the sea"
11. End of Sherman's "march to the sea"
12. State that divided over slavery
13. Union paper money

DOWN: _____

1. Lincoln's decision to free the slaves *(two words)*

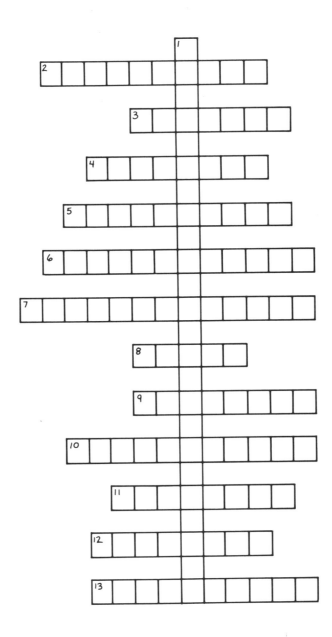

31. BATTLES OF THE CIVIL WAR

ACROSS: _____

2. Southern city captured by Admiral David Farragut

8. Bloody battle in western Tennessee

9. Battle that began the Civil War

11. Battle in which Stonewall Jackson was wounded and later died

12. "High water mark" of the Confederacy

13. Battle that began Sherman's "March to the Sea"

DOWN: _____

1. Battle in which General Burnside and the Army of the Potomac were defeated

3. Final battle and surrender location

4. Battle that completed the splitting of the Confederacy

5. Bloody battle in Maryland

6. Battle along Sherman's "March to the Sea"

7. Location of two Civil War battles

10. Battle that captured the Confederate capital

32. MEN AND WOMEN OF THE CIVIL WAR

ACROSS:

8. Confederate leader at Chancellorsville
10. Confederate nurse
12. Union leader at Machanicsville
13. Union spy
15. Union leader at Fredericksburg
16. Youngest Union general
18. Union leader at Bull Run
19. President of the United States
20. Confederate leader at Gettysburg
22. Union leader at Chancellorsville
23. Confederate leader at Chattanooga
25. "Tardy George"
29. Last Confederate general to surrender
30. Union naval leader
31. Union commander at Fort Sumter
33. "The butcher"

34. Confederate leader at Shiloh
35. Confederate leader at Chickamauga
36. Confederate leader at Bull Run
39. Confederate general at Gettysburg
42. Confederate general at Bull Run
43. Assassin of President Lincoln
45. Union general at Atlanta
46. "March to the Sea"
50. Union leader at Richmond
52. "J.E.B."
53. Confederate general at Gettysburg
54. Union nurse
55. Union leader at Gettysburg
56. Union leader at Chancellorsville
57. Union leader at Shiloh

DOWN:

1. Union leader at Vicksburg
2. "You have lost only your left arm while I have lost my right"
3. Commander of the Confederate Army
4. Union leader at Gettysburg
5. Vice-president of Abraham Lincoln
6. Union leader at Chancellorsville
7. Confederate commander at Fort Sumter
9. Vice-president of the Confederacy
11. Union general at Chattanooga
14. "War is hell"
17. "Sic semper tyrannus"
19. Confederate leader at Richmond
21. Union nurse
22. "Fighting Joe"
24. Confederate general at Gettysburg

26. Gettysburg Address
27. Confederate leader at Antietam
28. Founder of the American Red Cross
32. Confederate general at Shiloh
33. "When in doubt, fight"
36. "Stonewall"
37. Confederate general at Gettysburg
38. Commander of Andersonville Prison
40. Union leader at Shenandoah Valley
41. Union nurse
44. President of Confederacy
47. Confederate general at Gettysburg
48. Confederate general at Chickamauga
49. Assassin of President Lincoln
51. "Honest _____"

32. Men and Women of the Civil War

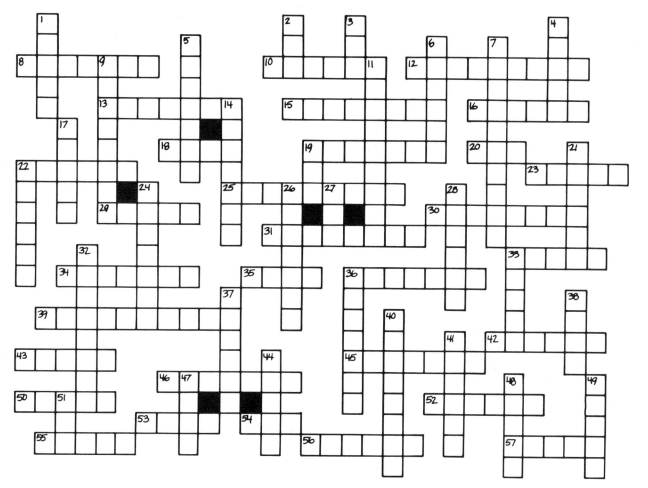

LINCOLN IN GEN. McCLELLAND'S TENT

33. SOUTHERN RECONSTRUCTION

ACROSS:

5. "_____ Ring"
8. "With malice toward none, with charity for all"
11. Vice-president of Abraham Lincoln
13. "Pitchfork Ben"; governor of South Carolina
17. Black _____
18. Southern state reconstructed in 1868 *(abbr.)*
19. President Grant's Secretary of War
20. Separation of blacks and whites
23. Leader of the Radical Republicans
28. Home state of Samuel J. Tilden *(abbr.)*
29. Southern state reconstructed in 1868 *(abbr.)*
30. President who ended reconstruction
33. Reconstruction president
36. _____-Davis Bill
37. Cash crop of the South
39. Reconstruction president
40. Number of terms for President Grant
42. Northerners who moved south after the Civil War

46. Government organization to help former slaves *(two words)*
49. Number of terms for President Johnson
50. Black senator from Mississippi
51. Plessy v. _____
54. Number of terms for President Hayes
56. Grand Wizard of the Ku Klux Klan
58. To charge a public official with misconduct
59. Number of terms for President Johnson
61. Black teacher for the Freedman's Bureau
62. Northern republicans who wanted to punish the South
67. State acts to segregate blacks in public facilities *(three words)*
68. Secret terrorist organization against blacks *(three words)*
69. "With _____ toward none"
70. "With _____ for all"
71. Southern state reconstructed in 1870
72. Southern state reconstructed in 1868 *(abbr.)*

DOWN:

1. Home state of President Grant
2. Southern state reconstructed in 1866 *(abbr.)*
3. Amendment that granted suffrage to blacks
4. White southerner in the Republican Party
6. Southern state reconstructed in 1868 *(abbr.)*
7. Name given to former slaves
9. Amendment that granted civil rights to blacks
10. Assassin of President Lincoln
12. Secretary of War fired by President Johnson
14. Pardon for crimes against the government
15. Southern state reconstructed in 1868 *(abbr.)*
16. Winner of the 1876 disputed presidential election
19. _____ v. Board of Education outlawed segregation
21. Home state of Thaddeus Stevens *(abbr.)*
22. Laws to regulate the economic and social life of freedom *(two words)*
24. "Separate but _____"
25. President Grant's private secretary
26. Southern state reconstructed in 1870 *(abbr.)*
27. Home state of President Hayes

31. Southern state reconstructed in 1868 *(abbr.)*
32. "Go _____, young man, go _____"
34. First state to be reconstructed
35. Amendment that abolished slavery
38. Farmer who payed his rent with a portion of his harvest
41. Scandal during President Grant's administration *(two words)*
43. Cash crop of the South
44. Black senator from Mississippi
45. Reconstruction president
48. "The country is going to the devil"
52. Southern state reconstructed in 1870 *(abbr.)*
53. Southern state reconstructed in 1870 *(abbr.)*
55. Home state of President Johnson *(abbr.)*
57. Democratic candidate in 1876
60. _____ v. Ferguson legalized segregation
63. Tax required before voting
64. Number of military districts in the South during Reconstruction
65. Ku _____ Klan
66. Ku Klux _____
68. Birthplace of President Lincoln *(abbr.)*

33. Southern Reconstruction

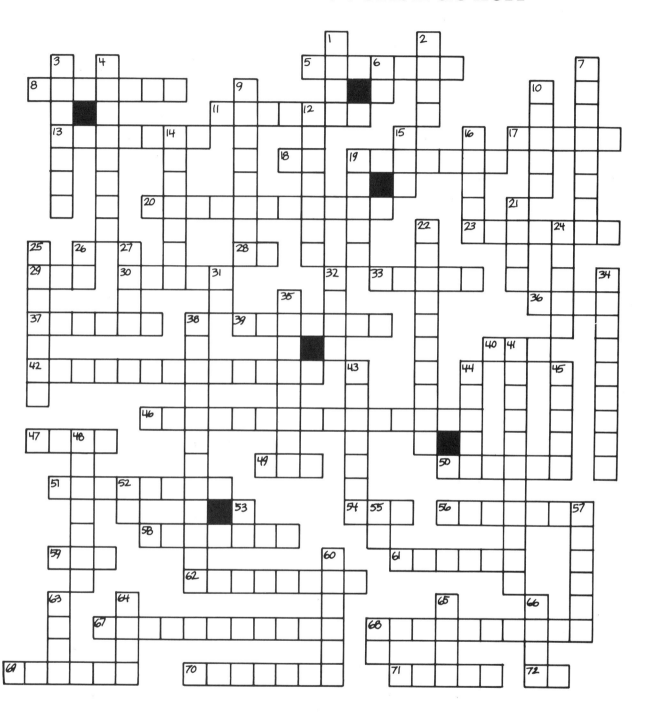

34. THE OLD WEST

ACROSS: _____

1. Martha Canary
3. Inventor of barbed wire
4. Army leader at the Battle of Little Big Horn
5. William F. Cody
6. Henry McCarty
7. Nat Love

8. Indian leader at the Battle of Little Big Horn
9. Inventor of the repeating pistol
10. Holder of the "Dead Man's Hand"
11. Indian leader at the Battle of Little Big Horn

DOWN: _____

2. First cowboy film *(four words)*

© 1993 by The Center for Applied Research in Education

Name _____ Date _____

35. AMERICAN INDIANS

ACROSS: _____

3. One of the Sioux leaders at Little Big Horn
7. Shawnee chief in the War of 1812
8. Son of Massasoit, known as "King Philip"
9. Chief of the Mohawks during the French and Indian War
10. Indian chief on Roanoke Island
12. Indian chief in Massachusetts
13. Chief of the Sac and the Fox Indians in Illinois
14. Indian who married Jamestown settler John Rolfe

DOWN: _____

1. Indian who helped the Pilgrims
2. Last Indian chief to surrender in Arizona
4. One of the Souix leaders at Little Big Horn
5. Brother of Tecumseh, known as "the Prophet"
6. Chief of the Seminole Indians in Florida
11. Chief of the Indians in Virginia

36. A NEW INDUSTRIAL AGE

1. "First Principles"
6. "Do and Dare"
8. Central Pacific Railroad
9. Union Pacific Railroad
10. Grant's vice-president
11. Inventor of barbed wire
14. Inventor of a steel-making process
16. Oil tycoon

21. "Wizard of Menlo Park"
23. Inventor of the typewriter
27. Inventor of the phonograph
29. Inventor of arc lights
31. Inventor of the tin can
34. Founder of the National Grange
35. Alexander _____ Bell
36. Co-owner of the first canning business

DOWN: _____

2. Inventor of the motion picture camera
3. Inventor of a steel-making process
4. Driller of the first oil well
5. Inventor of the telephone
7. Founder of the Grange
12. Author of the theory of natural selection
13. Co-owner of the first canning business
15. Inventor of the microphone
17. Inventor of the railroad sleeping car
18. Inventor of the light bulb
19. Mark Twain

20. Inventor of the telegraph
22. Builder of the first power station
24. Union Pacific Railroad
25. Inventor of the dynamo
26. Steel tycoon
28. Developer of time zones
30. Inventor of the gasoline-powered automobile
32. Inventor of a steel-making process
33. "Luck and Pluck"

© 1993 by The Center for Applied Research in Education

36. A New Industrial Age

37. CITIES AND BIG BUSINESS

ACROSS:

1. Keeping track of business costs
5. _____ houses
8. Nineteenth-century novelist
9. Eleven percent of immigrants came from this country
10. Author of *How the Other Half Lives*
14. NEA speaker
15. Mass _____
17. Philanthropist
18. _____ Island; immigration station
21. American _____ Association
22. Muckraker
23. Telephone inventor
24. New York school superintendent
26. Education philosopher
28. Founder of Hull House
29. Electric street car
30. Samuel Clemens
31. Circus owner
32. National Education Association *(abbr.)*
34. Fresh _____ Camps for city children
36. _____ of Italy; immigration organization
39. Run-down areas of a city
40. Jewish street language
42. _____ Bill Cody; Wild West Show owner
43. _____ of Italy
45. American Medical Association *(abbr.)*

46. Jewish language
47. Turn-of-the-century artist
51. Association of lawyers
52. Poor section of a city
53. Wild West Show performer
54. Crowded city apartment buildings
57. _____ and Bailey; circus owners
59. Telegraph inventor
60. Fresh _____ Camps
61. Isolation of a disease
64. Improved the sewing machine
65. Philanthropist
68. First college of business
69. _____ National Alliance
70. Sons of _____; immigration group
75. Railroad inventor
77. _____ Exclusion Act
80. Early factory owners' nickname
81. Thirteen percent of immigrants came from this country
83. Study of American government
84. Immigration island
85. American _____ Association
86. Philanthropist
87. Philanthropist
88. Inventor of the locomotive

DOWN:

2. President who served at two different times
3. Education group *(abbr.)*
4. Panama Canal engineer
5. Shakespearean actor
6. New York doctor
7. Education philosopher
11. Business of Andrew Carnegie
12. _____ House
13. _____ Air Camps
16. Phonograph inventor
19. Able to speak two languages
20. National Education Association *(abbr.)*
22. Ten percent of immigrants came from this country
25. American Bar Association *(abbr.)*
26. Turn-of-the-century novelist
27. Twelve percent of immigrants came from this country
28. Founder of Hull House
33. People who expose problems
35. Different ways of pronouncing words
36. Famous British playwright
37. Education group *(abbr.)*
38. "There's a sucker born every minute"
41. Education philosopher

44. Donating money to other people
48. Improved the sewing machine
49. Famous circus elephant
50. Early factory nickname
55. Six percent of immigrants came from this country
56. Author of *How the Other Half Lives*
58. Telegraph inventor
61. Limit on immigration
62. Attorney's group *(abbr.)*
63. Doctor who wiped out malaria
66. Mark Twain
67. Nationality group
71. Guaranteed job
72. Sixteen percent of immigrants came from this country
73. _____ and Bailey Circus
74. One of the first major wholesalers
75. Buffalo Bill _____
76. Telephone inventor
78. Methods of communication
79. Cotton gin inventor
82. A very wealthy person
85. American _____ Association

37. Cities and Big Business

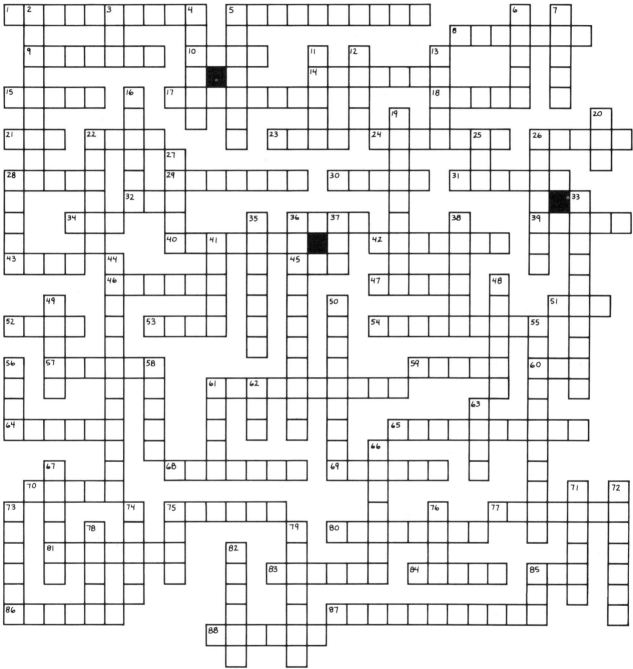

38. WORKERS AND UNIONS

ACROSS:

9. "Children's March"
10. President during the "Children's March"
12. American Federation of Labor
15. Railroad sleeping and dining cars
16. New York Factory Investigating Commission
17. Being paid by the amount of work produced
18. First woman cabinet member
19. International Ladies Garment Workers Union
22. Industrial Workers of the World
24. "Yellow _____" contract
26. National Colored Labor Union
30. Haymarket Riot
34. Refusal to work

36. Industrial detective agency
39. "_____" Jones
42. Early factory worker's nickname
43. Union of all types of workers
44. National Labor Union (abbr.)
45. Carnegie Steel Company
46. National Labor Union
49. Members of the Industrial Workers of the World
51. Names of union members and strikers
53. Grand Master of the Knights of Labor
55. President during the Pullman Strike
56. Factory using union and non-union workers
57. People who work during a strike

DOWN:

1. President of the New York Cigarmakers Union
2. Contract pledging not to join a union
3. Children working in coal mines (two words)
4. American Railway Union
5. People who work during a strike (two words)
6. Settling disagreements by a third party
7. Haymarket Riot
8. Striker's demonstration
11. Founder of the first labor union
13. Laundry Workers Union
14. Union Pacific Railroad
20. Early factory nickname
21. NLU
23. Attorney General of President Cleveland
25. New York Factory Investigating Commission

27. U.S. lawyer during the Pullman Strike
28. Closing a factory to union members
29. Knights of Labor
31. Location of the Haymarket Riot
32. Federation of Organized Trade and Labor Unions
33. Haymarket Riot
35. Court order prohibiting a strike
37. Oyster Bay, Long Island
38. Strikebreakers
40. Haymarket Riot
41. Union of only skilled workers
46. "An injury to one is the concern of all"
47. American Federation of Labor (abbr.)
48. Factory using only union workers
50. National Labor Union (abbr.)
52. Skill
54. Brotherhood of Locomotive Firemen and Enginemen

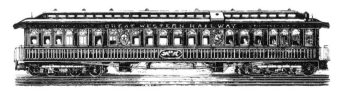

Name

Date

38. Workers and Unions

39. THE PROGRESSIVE ERA

ACROSS:

2. Young Men's Christian Association
6. "New Freedom" president
8. *History of the Standard* _____ *Company*
11. Muller v. Oregon
13. _____-Aldrich Tariff
14. Democratic candidate in 1904
16. "Square Deal" president
17. Socialist Party candidate
20. "Rough Riders" leader
23. Reform mayor
24. "_____ Riders"
26. Reading Railroad
27. "Uncle _____"
29. Roosevelt's successor
34. "Hard-boiled hayseed"
35. "A horse-drawn carriage"
36. Oregon governor
39. Act that outlawed railroad rebates
40. "Golden Rule" mayor
41. Muller v. Oregon

43. *Making Steel and Killing* _____
44. National Parks supervisor
46. "_____ Freedom"
48. *Making Steel and Killing Men*
49. _____ v. Oregon
53. Child labor critic
58. Assassinated president
60. "Don't flinch, don't foul, and hit the line hard"
61. "Square _____"
62. Bull Moose Party candidate
63. Young Women's Christian Association
66. *The Jungle*
68. *Pilgrim's Progress*
70. "_____ Deal"
72. Patent medicine critic
73. Pure _____ and Drug Act
74. Factory sanitation critic
75. "Social gospel" minister

DOWN:

1. "Triple wall of privilege"
3. _____ v. Oregon
4. "Speak softly and carry a big stick"
5. Democratic candidate in 1908
6. Pure Food and Drug Act
7. Underwood-_____ Tariff Act
9. Secretary of the Interior
10. Act that set maximum railroad rates
12. Socialist
15. "Holy Hiram"
18. Grand Old Party (abbr.)
19. Bunting v. _____
21. Act that outlawed railroad rebates
22. "Well-meaning man who was born with two left feet"
25. "Smiling Bill"
26. Muller v. Oregon
28. "Uncle Joe"
30. *History of the Standard Oil Company*
31. *The Shame of the Cities*
32. Railroad critic

33. New York governor
37. Missouri governor
38. Iowa governor
42. Minnesota governor
45. "Fighting Bob"
47. Patent medicine critic
50. Railroad critic
51. *Making Steel and Killing Men*
52. Oregon governor
54. North Carolina governor
55. Magazine editor
56. *The Gould Fortune*
57. *Making* _____ *and Killing Men*
59. *Frenzied Finance*
64. Reform mayor
65. *The* _____ *Fortune*
67. Socialist
68. Reading Railroad
69. Young Men's Christian Association
71. "Smiling _____"
72. "Fighting _____"

39. The Progressive Era

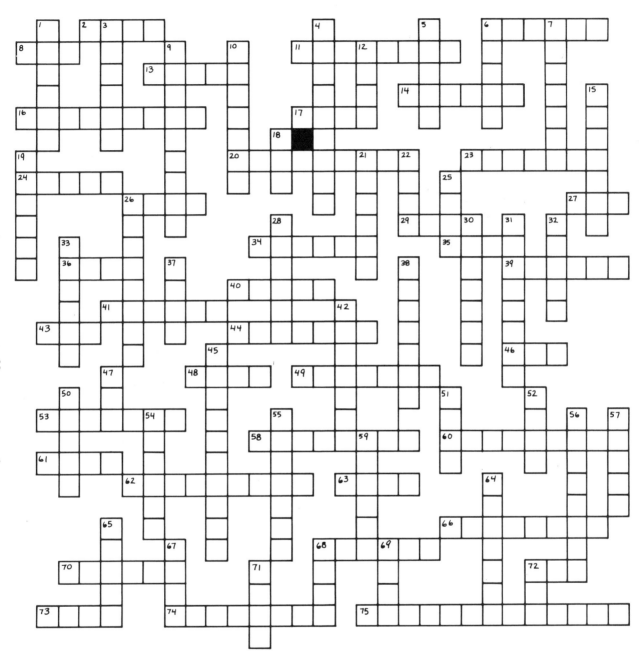

40. THE GILDED AGE

ACROSS:

2. Heavyweight boxing champion in 1897
7. Millionaire
8. Millionaire
9. American reporter in Africa
10. Bicycle producer
13. African explorer
14. "The Swedish Nightingale"
16. Tuskegee Institute
17. "Boston Strong Boy"
21. "Mile a minute"
22. Millionaire
24. Kodak camera
26. Theater owner
27. Millionaire
32. Mark Twain

33. Web printing press
36. French actress
37. Inventor of baseball
41. Bicycle producer
42. *New York Journal* editor
44. "The Masked Ball"
45. Heavyweight boxing champion in 1892
48. Elizabeth Cochrane
49. Theater owner
50. Found new uses for the peanut
51. Samuel Clemens
52. *The Red Badge of Courage*
53. Heavyweight boxing champion in 1899
54. Built a university in Nashville, Tennessee

DOWN:

1. "Mutt and Jeff"
2. Theater producer
3. Linotype machine
4. *Around the World in Eighty Days*
5. *The Rise of Silas Lapham*
6. *The Promised Land*
11. *Around the World in Eighty Days* reporter
12. *Peter Pan*
15. *New York World* editor
17. Wainwright Building
18. *The Red Badge of Courage*
19. Philanthropist
20. *The Honest Blacksmith*
23. *The Adventures of Tom Sawyer*

25. Electric readers
28. Millionaire
29. Nellie Bly
30. *New York World* reporter
31. French actress
32. "Gentleman Jack"
34. Botanist
35. English actress
38. Shakespearean actor
39. *Sister Carrie*
40. Shakespearean actor
43. *Honest Hearts and Willing Hands*
45. Found new uses for the sweet potato
46. Millionaire
47. "Gentleman Jim"

40. The Gilded Age

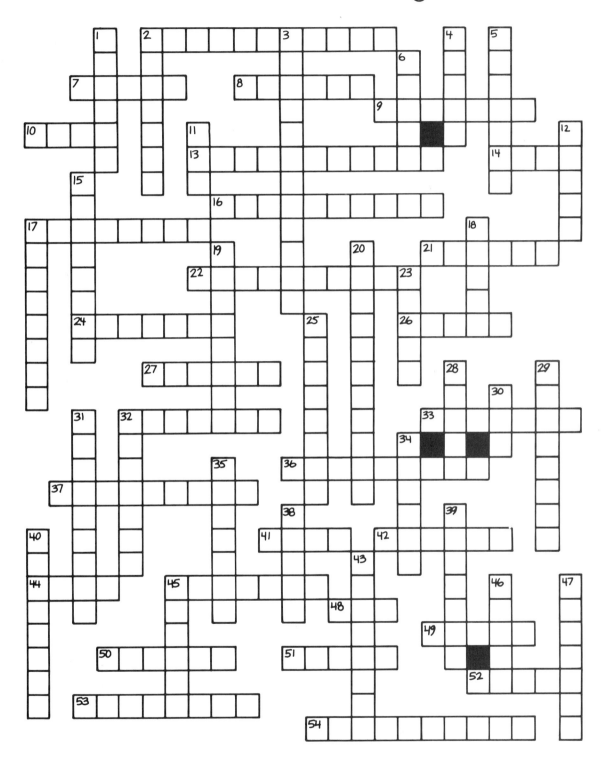

41. THE SPANISH-AMERICAN WAR

ACROSS:

1. President when U.S. got Pearl Harbor
9. Leader of the Filipino rebels
10. President during the war
11. Pago _____
13. U.S. naval base in Samoa
14. U.S. naval base in Cuba
16. Chinese against foreign trade
17. Key _____, Florida
21. U.S. ship sunk in the war
22. Made Open Door Policy with China
23. Commander of the U.S.S. Maine
24. _____ Jaun
26. American governor of the Philippines
27. _____ American Conference
28. Narrow strip of land between bodies of water
32. Major crop of Cuba
33. Location of the first battle

35. Treaty to trade with Japan
37. People of the Philippines
39. Naval base in Hawaii *(two words)*
41. Spanish ambassador to the U.S.
43. U.S. naval leader in the war
44. U.S. army leader in the war
45. First American to visit Japan
46. Editor of the *New York Journal*
50. _____ American Conference
51. "_____ journalism"
54. Country that revolted against Spain
56. Spanish naval leader in the war
57. Island halfway across the Pacific Ocean
59. Islands off the coast of Florida *(two words)*
60. Nickname of Roosevelt's soldiers *(two words)*
61. First American to visit Japan

DOWN:

2. Last queen of Hawaii
3. Spanish ambassador who criticized President McKinley
4. Location of San Juan Hill
5. _____ Juan Hill
6. "_____ Riders"
7. Puerto _____
8. _____ Harbor
11. Location of canal to connect oceans
12. Island taken from Spain in the war
15. U.S. naval leader in the Philippines
17. Key _____
18. _____ Juan
19. Location of the Pan American Conference
20. Governor of the Philippines
23. Island taken away from Spain in the war
25. American hero of the war

29. Harbor blocked in the war
30. Capital of the Philippines
31. Trade policy with China *(two words)*
34. Goods bought by a country
36. "Remember the _____"
38. Cuban hill captured by Roosevelt
40. Goods sold by a country
42. U.S.S. _____
45. Editor of the *New York World*
47. Major crop of Cuba
48. _____ Rico
49. Nickname of General Weyler
50. _____ Pago
52. Spanish army leader in the war
53. U.S. Secretary of State during the war
55. U.S. military leader in Puerto Rico
58. _____ West

© 1993 by The Center for Applied Research in Education

41. The Spanish-American War

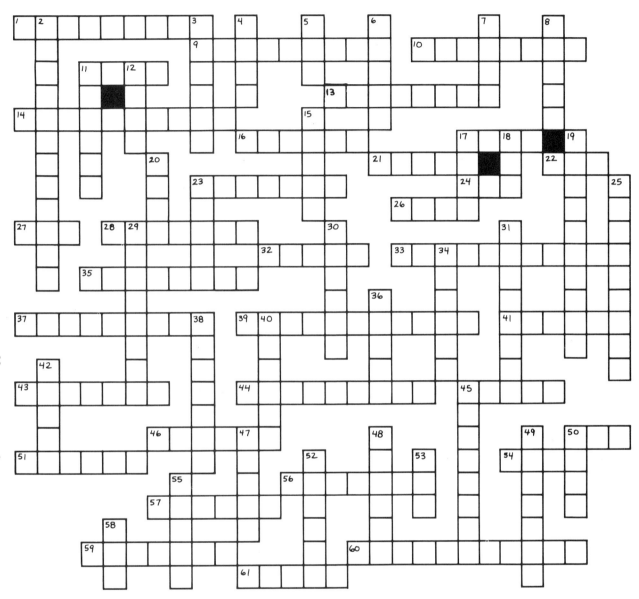

42. THE PANAMA CANAL

ACROSS:

4. Home state of President Wilson *(abbr.)*
7. President who returned the canal zone to Panama
8. Years for constructing the canal
9. Disease of Panama
11. Home state of President Roosevelt *(abbr.)*
12. Panamanian minister to the United States
13. Home state of President Carter *(abbr.)*

14. U.S. Secretary of State
16. Narrow strip of land
18. Original owner of Panama
22. First country to attempt a canal across Panama
23. U.S. president when the canal was begun
24. U.S. doctor in Panama
25. Miles in width of the Canal Zone

DOWN:

1. Amendment giving the U.S. the right of intervention in Panama
2. U.S. engineer in Panama
3. _____-Varilla Treaty
4. Bunau-_____ Treaty
5. Capital city of Panama
6. Disease spread by mosquitoes
10. _____-Bunau-Varilla Treaty

11. U.S. battleship in Panama
15. Panama seaport
17. U.S. president when the canal was completed
18. U.S. president
19. Panama seaport
20. _____ Amendment
21. Walter _____ Army Hospital

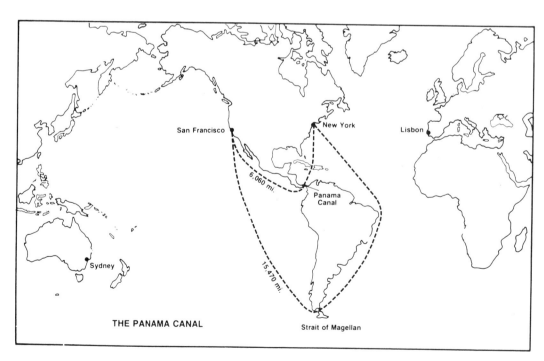

THE PANAMA CANAL

Name _____   Date _____

42. The Panama Canal

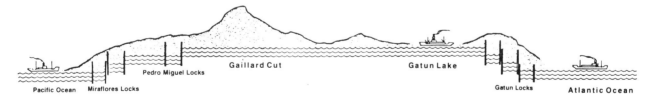

Panama Canal Locks: This diagram shows a cross-section of the locks of the
Panama Canal connecting the Atlantic and the Pacific Oceans.

Pacific Ocean   Miraflores Locks   Pedro Miguel Locks   Gaillard Cut   Gatun Lake   Gatun Locks   Atlantic Ocean

43. WORLD WAR I

ACROSS:

6. German general in WWI
8. Russian communists
15. British ship sunk by the Germans
16. Italian leader in WWI
17. "Uncle _____"
19. Central Power in WWI
21. Name of the countries against Germany
22. French general in WWI
24. British leader in WWI
25. Leader of the Bolshevik Revolution
26. Name of the enemy countries in WWI
27. Nickname of the American war symbol
30. U.S. leader for war conservation
31. Famous battle of WWI
35. "Uncle _____"
37. American naval leader in WWI
38. Allied country in WWI
40. Assassin of Archduke Ferdinand
42. "_____ Freedom"

43. Nickname of President Wilson's term *(two words)*
45. Mexican leader in WWI
47. "Freedom of the _____"
48. Member of the "Big Four"
52. Leader of Austria-Hungary in WWI
54. Chairman of the Senate Foreign Relations Committee
56. U.S. naval leader in WWI
58. Member of the "Big Four"
59. "_____ Sam"
60. German submarine
64. American military leader in WWI
66. Popular war song *(two words)*
67. French river
68. Central Power in WWI
69. U.S. naval leader
70. Henry Cabot _____

DOWN:

1. Central power in WWI *(two words)*
2. Treaty to end WWI
3. Submarine
4. "_____ Freedom"
5. Nickname of American soldiers
7. Number of President Wilson's "Points"
9. American naval leader
10. "Uncle _____"
11. Allied Power in WWI
12. German ambassador to Mexico
13. Location of Ferdinand's assassination
14. "Reds"
18. Allied Power of WWI
20. German "leader"
23. American President during WWI
24. "Government Issue" *(abbr.)*
26. Location of German surrender
28. Popular war song *(two words)*
29. Archduke of Austria-Hungary

32. Allied Power in WWI
33. British ship sunk by Germany
34. German leader in WWI
36. French leader in WWI
39. _____ Powers
41. Allied Power in WWI
44. Supreme Allied Commander in WWI
46. _____ Wilhelm
49. French general in WWI
50. "Blackjack"
51. Leader of Austria-Hungary in WWI
53. U.S. nickname *(two words)*
55. Allied Power in WWI
57. "_____ Pledge"
61. "_____ Freedom"
62. Famous WWI battle
63. U-_____
65. U.S. naval leader in WWI

43. World War I

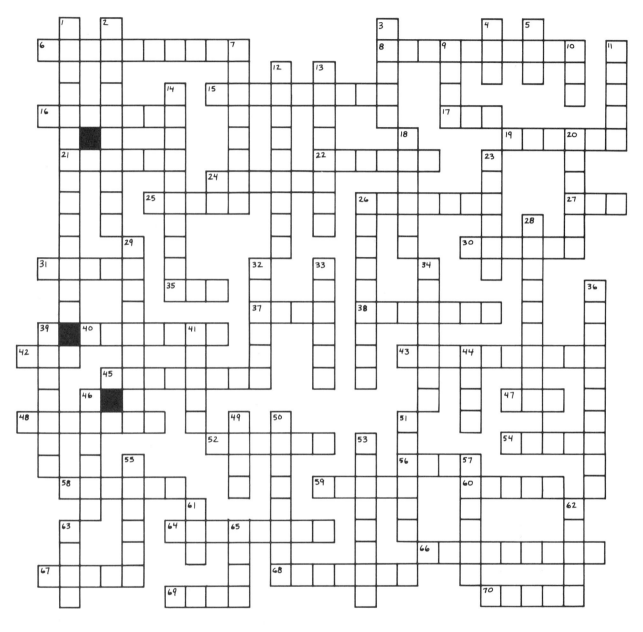

44. THE ROARING 20'S AND THE GREAT DEPRESSION

ACROSS:

3. A refusal to buy or use
5. Illegal tavern
9. First woman elected to Congress
10. Organizer of the Women's Party
13. Ku _____ Klan
14. Communists
16. Radical immigrant who was executed
18. Birthplace of Jazz
20. First motion picture (four words)
23. Girls' nickname of the 1920's
24. Black writer of the 1920's
26. A refusal to buy or use
28. _____ Smith
31. The period of forbidden drinking
33. The Red _____
35. First radio station
37. Evangelist of the 1920's
39. White, Anglo-Saxon, Protestant (abbr.)
40. Gangster of the 1920's
42. Critical painter of the 1920's
44. One of the first Black colleges
46. First airplane flight to the North Pole
48. Star of the first talking picture
49. Good, run-down neighborhood
52. President Harding's Secretary of the Interior
53. Boxing hero of the 1920's and 1930's
55. _____ Klux Klan
56. The Jazz _____
57. "The Jazz _____"

58. Target of the Ku Klux Klan
60. The _____ Scare
65. "The Galloping Ghost"
66. Black musician of the 1920's
68. Black author of the 1920's
70. Radical immigrant who was executed
72. _____ Grange
74. Black author of the 1920's
76. _____ Faire
77. President of the National Woman Suffrage Association
78. "_____ Deal"
80. Builder of the Model T
82. Nickname of Oklahoma in the 1930's (two words)
84. Black author of the 1920's
85. Ku _____ Klan
86. Baseball hero of the 1920's and 1930's
87. Dance of the 1920's
88. President of the National Woman Suffrage Association
91. Golf hero of the 1920's
93. Founder of the Committee for Industrial Organization
94. _____ Jolson
97. Inventor of the automobile
98. First talking movie, The _____ _____
99. Nickname of the day of the Stock Market crash (two words)

DOWN:

1. Famous female aviator
2. A foreign revolutionary
4. Tennis hero of the 1920's and 1930's
5. Teacher convicted of teaching evolution
6. Black leader in the 1920's
7. First transatlantic airplane flight
8. _____ Klux Klan
11. Organized the National Woman Suffrage Association
12. Black author of the 1920's
15. One of the first Black colleges
16. Organized the National Woman Suffrage Association
17. Home state of President Harding
19. The Spirit of _____
21. Target of the Ku Klux Klan
22. The _____ Gang
25. Democratic candidate in 1928 election
27. Oil scandal under President Harding (two words)
29. The Jazz Singer
30. Radio singer of the 1920's and 1930's
32. Nickname of the 1920's
34. "The Sultan of Swat"
36. Inventor of frozen foods
38. "_____ Deal"

41. Black section of New York City
51. Russian leader
52. Laissez _____
53. Inventor of plastic
54. The _____ of St. Louis
59. Radio comedian of the 1920's and 1930's
61. Inventor of plastic
62. The _____ Singer
63. Center of the movie industry
64. Limit of immigrants
67. Organized the Universal Negro Improvement Association
69. Target of the Ku Klux Klan
71. Inventor of the time-and-motion study
73. "Hoover blankets"
75. _____ Klux Klan
79. Brothers who started the movie industry
81. Ku Klux _____
83. Movie comedian of the 1920's and 1930's
89. Black author of the 1920's
90. Tennis hero of the 1920's
92. Democratic presidential candidate in 1928
95. Convicted in the Teapot Dome Scandal
96. _____ Valee

44. The Roaring 20's and the Great Depression

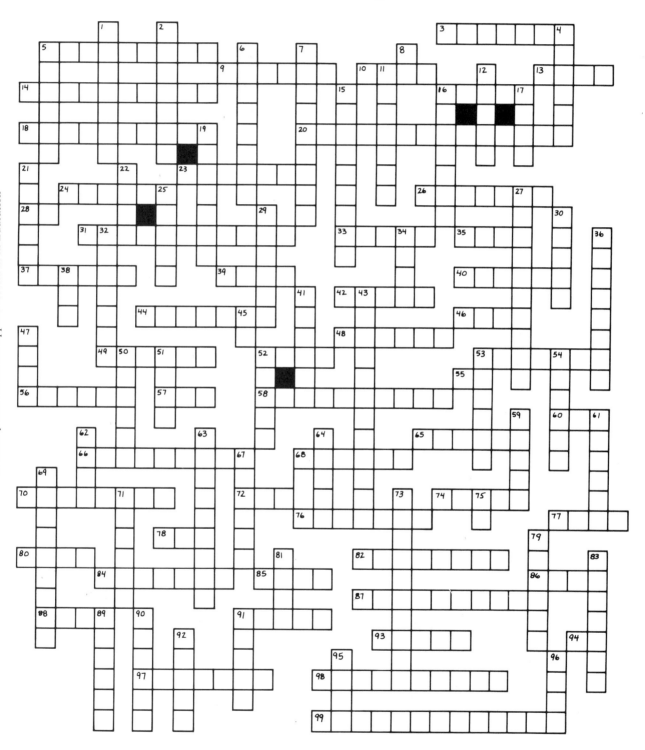

45. THE NEW DEAL

ACROSS:

2. Famous female aviator
8. Founder of the Committee for Industrial Organization
10. American Federation of Labor *(abbr.)*
11. President Roosevelt *(abbr.)*
12. Navajo tribal chief
15. Chief Justice of the Supreme Court under President Roosevelt
16. Program to control businesses and labor *(abbr.)*
17. Roosevelt had been President Wilson's Secretary of _____
18. Tennessee River dam project *(abbr.)*
20. Dance of the Navajo Indians
22. Welfare
24. Nickname of Oklahoma during the depression *(two words)*
26. This produces electricity from waterfalls
28. Collective name for newspapers, radio, and so on
29. Program to conserve resources *(abbr.)*
35. Political party of President Roosevelt
36. Mass _____
37. Tennessee Valley Authority *(abbr.)*
39. Labor union *(abbr.)*
40. Program to help farmers *(abbr.)*
42. Law protecting union members from being fired
43. Navajo leader who wanted to modernize Indians
44. Program to put needy students to work *(abbr.)*

DOWN:

1. Program to help pay mortgages *(abbr.)*
3. Black singer during the depression
4. "New Deal" President
5. Mrs. Roosevelt
6. Program to build public projects
7. Indian tribe of Chee Dodge
9. One who travels to find work
13. Home Owners Loan Corporation *(abbr.)*
14. Home state of President Roosevelt *(abbr.)*
19. Labor union *(abbr.)*
21. Illness of President Roosevelt
23. Bank insurance corporation *(abbr.)*
25. Program for national work projects
27. First dam built by the TVA
28. Loan on a house
30. Commissioner of Indian Affairs under Roosevelt
31. President Roosevelt *(abbr.)*
32. Chairman of Roosevelt's relief program
33. First female cabinet member
34. Law to protect workers from firing
38. Agricultural Adjustment Act *(abbr.)*
41. Program to give work to the unemployed

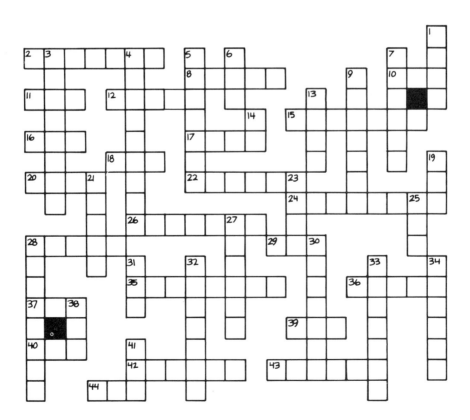

Name _____   Date _____

46. NEW DEAL ABBREVIATIONS

ACROSS:

2. Limited production in industry
4. Protected bank deposits
7. Regulated bank transactions
10. Required manufacturers to list ingredients of their products
12. Industrial unions
14. Promoted efficiency and savings in light and power companies
15. Craft unions
16. Created a pension system for retired workers
17. Established to prevent rigging of the stock market
18. Paid farmers for land left unseeded
19. Government-created jobs

DOWN:

1. Set up codes for fair competition in industry
2. Provided job training for unemployed students
3. Helped states provide jobs for the unemployed
4. Provided loans for building and repairing houses
5. Employed single males to build roads and plant trees
6. Provided federal loans for home improvement
8. Provided cheap electricity for isolated areas
9. Gave low-interest loans to homeowners
10. Set up minimum wages and maximum hours
11. Created work in federal jobs
13. Built dams for flood control and hydroelectric power
14. Government-created jobs

47. WORLD WAR II

ACROSS:

5. British prime minister during WWII
8. Site of the Allied evacuation of France
11. Execution of the Jews
13. Battle of the _____
15. Japanese emperor during WWII
17. Site of the Japanese attack on Hawaii (*two words*)
18. "The _____ Fox"
19. British general during WWII
23. Join the army
24. Black magazine first published during WWII
27. _____-Lease Act
32. Code name for the Allied invasion of France
33. Battle site in Russia
35. England's air force (*abbr.*)
36. Regular army (*abbr.*)
38. Japanese general during WWII
39. Political party of Adolf Hitler
40. American-born Japanese
42. U.S. ship sunk at Pearl Harbor
43. "The Desert _____"
46. Battle site in the Pacific
47. Loan to the government
49. Royal Air Force (*abbr.*)
51. U.S. president when WWII ended
54. American general in the Pacific
58. War _____
59. Peace conference site of WWII
61. Name given to the countries fighting against Germany
62. General Eisenhower (*nickname*)
64. Famous Japanese-American soldier
66. Black organization formed during WWII
69. U.S. ship on which the Japanese surrendered
70. Location of the Allied evacuation of France
71. Drafted soldier (*abbr.*)
72. British king during WWII
73. Presidential candidate in 1944
75. Enemy country during WWII
77. Site of atomic bombing
80. _____ Harbor
81. Women's Army Corps (*abbr.*)
82. Site of atomic bombing
84. Enlisted soldier (*abbr.*)
86. Female soldiers (*abbr.*)
88. Chairman of the War Production Board
94. Government issue (*abbr.*)
96. General Rommel's nickname
97. Women Appointed for Voluntary Emergency Service (*abbr.*)
98. German "lightning warfare"
99. Female volunteers
101. Black magazine published during WWII
103. Iwo _____
104. "I like _____"
107. "Victory over Japan" day
109. Battle site in the Philippines
111. American general in Africa
112. Capital of Germany
114. Invasion of Normandy code name
115. Canal connecting Mediterranean Sea and Red Sea
116. Battle site in the Pacific
119. Author of *Negro Digest*
121. WWII peace conference location
122. Underwater detector
123. Execution of the Jews
124. Russian leader during WWII
125. German in charge of executing the Jews
126. "The Desert _____"
127. American general in the Pacific

DOWN:

1. U.S. President when WWII began
2. "The Desert Fox"
3. Female soldier
4. Japanese-Americans born in Japan
6. German leader during WWII
7. Aircraft-detecting device
9. Chiang _____-shek
10. "Victory in Europe" day
12. American naval leader during WWII
14. Black magazine published during WWII
16. German in charge of the Gestapo
20. "I shall return" general
21. Bloody battle fought in Belgium
22. Enemy country during WWII
25. Name given to the enemy countries
26. Lend-_____ Act
28. Famous battle fought in the Philippines
29. British king during WWII
30. Bloody battle site in Italy
31. Bloody battle site in the Philippines
33. Underwater detecting device
34. Bloody battle site in Italy
37. Republican candidate in 1940
41. _____ Jima
43. Spanish leader during WWII
44. Battle site in the Pacific
45. To limit products during wartime
48. Enemy country during WWII
50. Russian leader during WWII
52. Allied invasion site in France
53. D-Day location
55. Female volunteer
56. German executioner of the Jews
57. Japanese naval leader during WWII
60. Famous battle site in the Pacific
63. American general during WWII
65. American aircraft, "Flying _____"
67. Italian leader during WWII
68. Japanese-Americans born in America
74. Battle site in Egypt
76. Japanese suicide pilot
78. Royal Air Force (*abbr.*)
79. Chinese leader during WWII
83. _____ Jima
85. Japanese general during WWII
87. Canal in the Middle East
89. American general during WWII
90. War supplies
91. American naval leader during WWII
92. French "underground" leader during WWII
93. Russian leader during WWII
95. Royal Air Force (*abbr.*)
100. May 8, 1945
102. Founder of the Pullman Car Workers Union during WWII
105. President when the atomic bombs were dropped on Japan
106. August 14, 1945
108. Victims of the Nazi Party
110. Battle site in the Pacific
111. Pennsylvania (*abbr.*)
113. Detecting device
117. Black magazine
118. Hitler's political party
120. Japanese general during WWII

Name ______________________________ Date ____________________

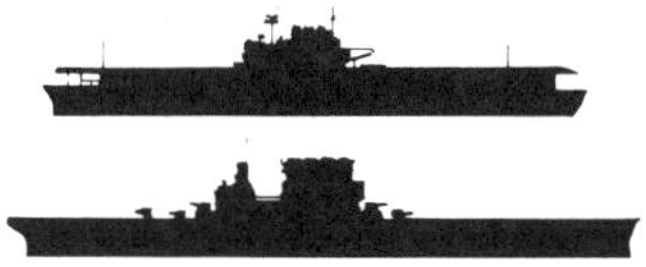

47. World War II

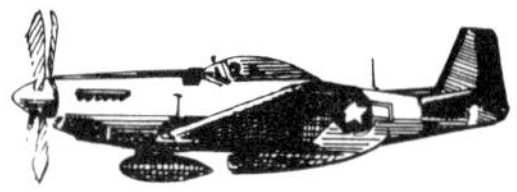

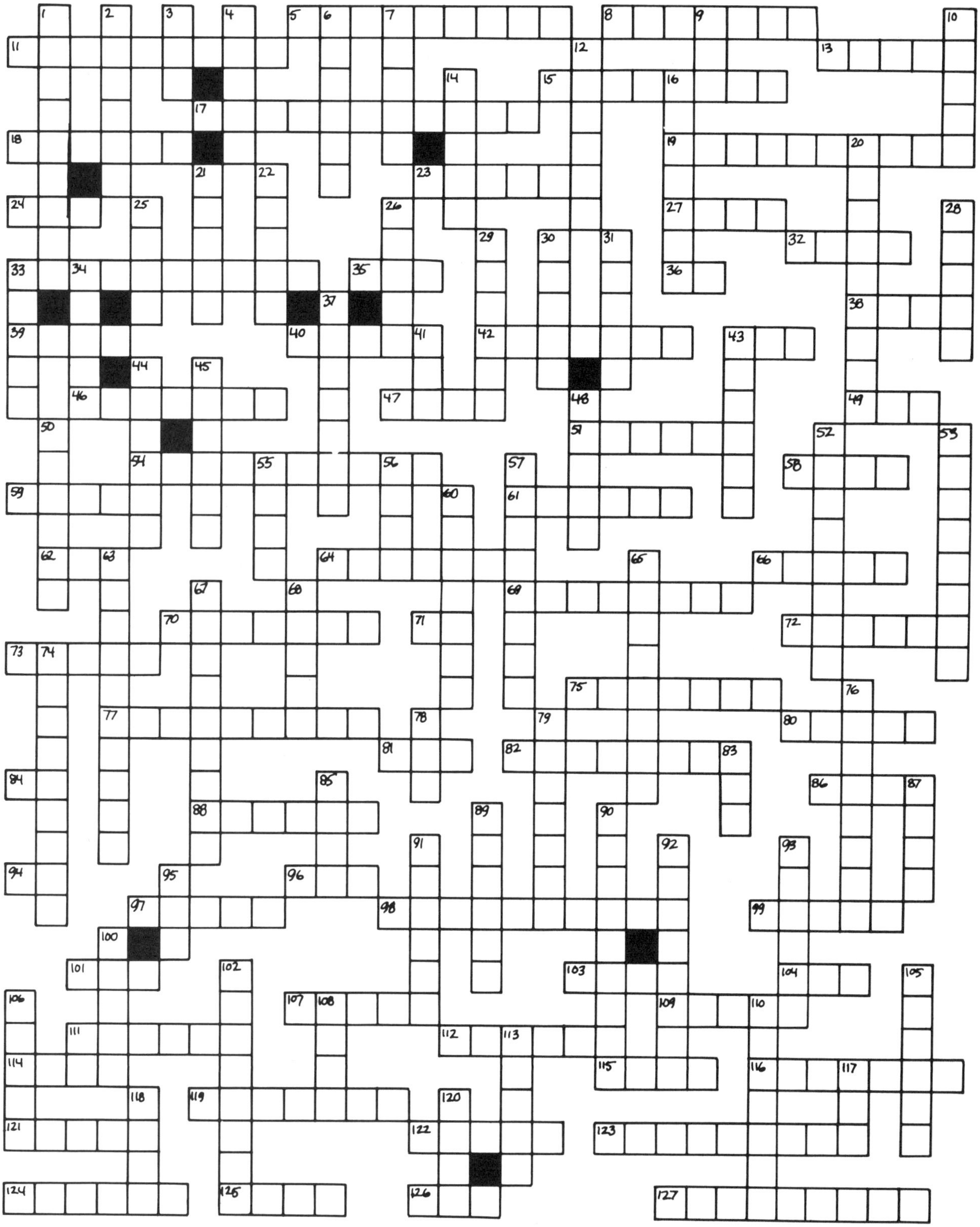

48. POST WORLD WAR II

ACROSS:

4. Leader of the Soviet Union
7. Baseball team of Jackie Robinson
9. Soviet foreign minister
10. Home state of President Truman (*abbr.*)
14. Capital of East Germany
15. "Government issue" (*abbr.*)
16. Countries dominated by the Soviet Union (*two words*)
18. California (*abbr.*)
20. U.S. policy to resist the spread of communism (*two words*)
21. Un-American Activities Committee of the House of Representatives (*abbr.*)
23. 1952 president-elect
25. 1948 presidential opponent of Harry Truman
28. Federal Republic of Germany

31. British spy who helped the communists
32. Organization to protect Western Europe from communism
34. Communist spy
35. Nickname of President Eisenhower
36. Location of the United Nations (*abbr.*)
37. First black elected to the Baseball Hall of Fame
39. International peace-keeping organization
40. Home state of Richard Nixon (*abbr.*)
41. "Get tough with Russia"
42. _____ Bill of Rights
43. President Truman's Secretary of State
44. Editor of *Time* Magazine
45. Anti-communist senator
46. Countries controlled by the Soviet Union
47. Soviet leader

DOWN:

1. Policy to keep communism from expanding
2. First black to play major league baseball
3. Capital of West Germany
5. President of the United Mine Workers Union
6. Location of the United Nations (*abbr.*)
8. Servicemen's Readjustment Act (*two words*)
10. Anti-communist senator
11. "_____ Curtain"
12. Born in the 1940's, this younger son of a performing family became a singing star in the 1950's
13. "The buck stops here"
14. Capital of West Germany

17. U.S. ambassador to the Soviet Union
19. Nickname of President Truman's administration (*two words*)
22. British leader
24. "I'm tired of babying the Soviets"
26. German Democratic Republic
27. "If you can't stand the heat, get out of the kitchen"
28. Organization to protect Eastern European countries (*two words*)
29. Nickname for an American soldier
30. Executed communist spies
33. "_____ Curtain"
38. "Give 'em hell, Harry"
40. American spy organization

48. Post World War II

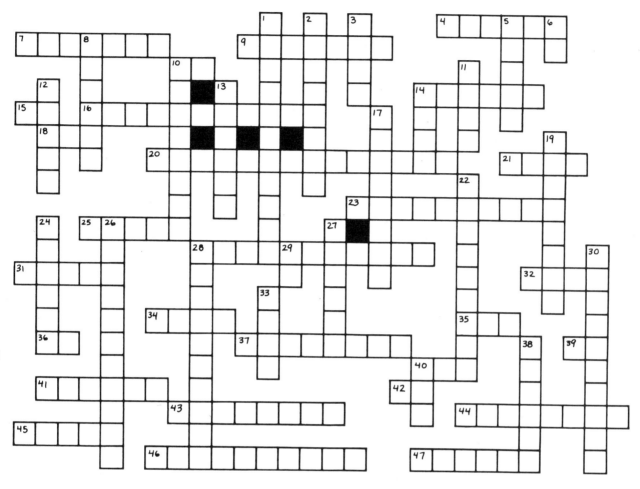

49. THE 1950's

ACROSS:

6. Capital of North Korea
8. *The Lone* _____
10. "_____ and roll"
11. 1950's singing group
17. Alliance of Western European allies (*abbr.*)
20. State added to the Union in 1959
22. Music of the 1950's (*three words*)
24. First black Supreme Court Justice
25. Nickname of President Eisenhower
26. 1950's Soviet leader
27. President during Korean War
29. 1950's rock-and-roll singer
30. Country that first colonized Vietnam
31. Black who sued for school integration
35. "Land of the Morning Calm"
36. "Rock Around the Clock"
38. Peace-keeping organization (*abbr.*)
41. *The* _____ *Ranger*
42. "The buck stops here"
44. Black who integrated Alabama buses

45. 1950's newscaster
49. North Atlantic Treaty Organization (*abbr.*)
51. 1950's president
54. "Heartbreak Hotel"
55. Number of terms for President Eisenhower
57. Site of 1957 racial violence
58. "I could do nothing else and still be President"
60. "If you can't stand the heat, get out of the kitchen"
63. "Ike"
66. Black who integrated Alabama buses
69. "Checkers" speech
70. "Rock and _____"
71. Allied alliance against communism (*abbr.*)
72. 1950's missile (*abbr.*)
74. 1950's newscaster
75. "You Ain't Nothin' but a Hound Dog"

DOWN:

1. First Soviet spacecraft
2. Home state of President Truman (*abbr.*)
3. Location of Little Rock (*abbr.*)
4. "_____ and roll"
5. "Sh-Boom"
7. Missouri (*abbr.*)
9. _____ Bill of Rights
12. "Toast of the Town" TV host
13. War fought during the 1950's
14. "I Love _____"
15. Leader of "The Comets"
16. "I like _____"
18. 1950's Chief Justice of the Supreme Court
19. 1950's children's TV show (*two words*)
21. Arkansas (*abbr.*)
23. President Eisenhower's Secretary of State
26. Civil rights leader
28. 1950's newscaster
30. Disc jockey who named "rock and roll"
32. Eisenhower's nickname
33. "Henry Ford of the housing industry"

34. 1950's popular TV show
37. 1950's Soviet leader
39. "Old soldiers never die, they just fade away"
40. "I like _____"
43. Home state of President Truman (*abbr.*)
46. *The* _____ *Ranger*
47. Country divided by communism in 1954
48. Home state of President Eisenhower
50. Vice-president of President Eisenhower
52. State added to the Union in 1959
53. Korean War general
56. 1950's black leader
59. *Howdy Doody* host: Cowboy _____
61. "A respectable Republican cloth coat"
62. 1950's rock-and-roll singer
64. Capital of South Korea
65. "Love Me Tender"
67. "It was a great ride"
68. Cowboy _____
73. Missouri (*abbr.*)

49. The 1950's

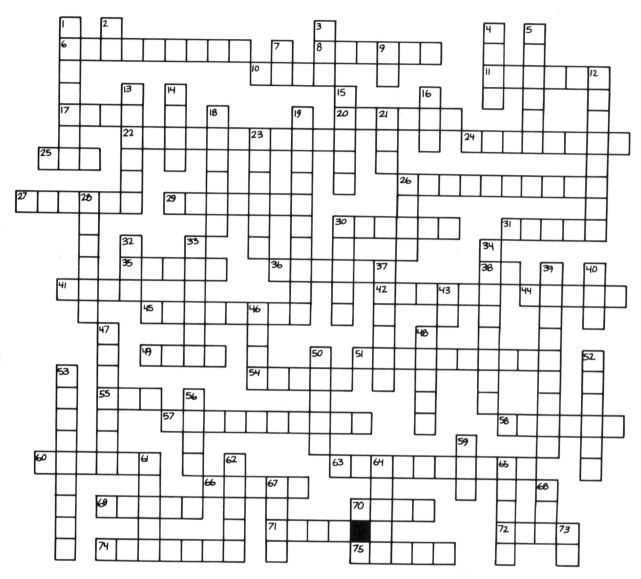

50. THE 1960's

ACROSS:

1. "Hot _____"
2. Location of President Kennedy's burial
5. _____ Start Program
8. "Flower child"
10. Wife of President Kennedy
12. Educational program for preschool children
15. Assassin of Martin Luther King, Jr.
17. "I have a dream"
19. American spy plane: U-_____
20. Religion of President Kennedy
22. Moon landing craft
23. U.S. space agency (*abbr.*)
24. Limit of terms for a U.S. President
25. Slain civil rights leader
26. Location of Robert Kennedy's assassination (*abbr.*)
27. Civil rights leader
28. National Organization for Women (*abbr.*)
30. Location of the 1968 Democratic Convention
33. Location of the Watts race riots (*abbr.*)
35. Peace-keeping organization (*abbr.*)
36. South Vietnam leader
39. U.S. naval base in Cuba
40. Vice-president of President Kennedy
41. Nuclear Test _____ Treaty
46. *Unsafe at Any Speed* author
47. Internal Revenue Service (*abbr.*)
49. Communication between the White House and the Kremlin
50. Kennedy's opponent in 1960
52. National Aeronautics and Space Administration (*abbr.*)
53. Nickname of President Johnson's administration (*two words*)

55. Location of an unsuccessful invasion of Cuba (*three words*)
58. First American astronaut
63. Assassin of Martin Luther King, Jr.
66. Slain NAACP leader
68. Assassin of Lee Harvey Oswald
69. Leader of the communist revolution in Cuba
71. National Organization for Women (*abbr.*)
72. 1960 Soviet leader
73. President Kennedy
75. Communist leader of Cuba
76. Volunteers who worked in underdeveloped nations (*two words*)
79. Assassin of Robert Kennedy
80. _____ of Pigs
81. Location of 1967 race riots
82. Economic program of President Johnson (*three words*)
85. Home state of Robert Kennedy (*abbr.*)
89. 1960's Soviet leader
90. The _____ Frontier
91. First black student admitted to the University of Mississippi
93. Organization to help blacks
95. Leader of the Black Panther Party
96. Long-haired teenagers of the 1960's
97. Attorney General of President Kennedy
98. Vietnamese New Year's Eve
101. Assassin of President Kennedy
102. Hospital insurance for the elderly
103. "Ask not what your country can do for you, ask what you can do for your country"

DOWN:

1. President Johnson
3. Lyndon Baines Johnson (*abbr.*)
4. Vietnamese war offensive
5. Department of Housing and Urban Development (*abbr.*)
6. Volunteers working in urban ghettos
7. Founder of the National Organization for Women
9. Lunar module spacecraft
11. Location of a 1960's race riot in California
13. Three-man spacecraft
14. Director of the FBI
16. U.S. space launch site (*two words*)
17. Youngest president ever elected
18. First American astronaut to orbit the earth
21. Home state of President Nixon (*abbr.*)
23. Nickname of President Kennedy's administration (*two words*)
27. Slain civil rights leader
29. American astronaut
30. Texas governor shot during Kennedy's assassination
31. Two-man spacecraft
32. First black cabinet member
34. Economic agency created by President Johnson (*abbr.*)
37. Home state of President Kennedy (*abbr.*)
38. Women's organization (*abbr.*)
42. Winner of the 1968 presidential election
43. Winner of the Kennedy-Nixon TV debates
44. Bay of _____
45. Head of the Peace Corps
48. Bay of _____
51. U.S. space control center

54. Location of the Houston Control Center (*abbr.*)
56. American spy pilot shot down over the Soviet Union
57. Paid school dropouts while training for employment (*two words*)
59. "One small step for man, one giant leap for mankind"
60. Location of President Kennedy's assassination
61. 1960's Chief Justice of the Supreme Court
62. One-man spacecraft
64. President Kennedy's nickname
65. John Fitzgerald Kennedy (*abbr.*)
67. American astronaut
70. Location of Cape Canaveral (*abbr.*)
73. Economic agency created by President Johnson (*two words*)
74. Location of President Kennedy's assassination
77. Congress of Racial Equality (*abbr.*)
78. Soviet spy traded for an American spy
81. Secretary of Housing and Urban Development
83. Presidential assassin killed by Jack Ruby
84. Location of Martin Luther King, Jr.'s assassination (*abbr.*)
85. Location of Martin Luther King, Jr.'s assassination
86. Founder of the Black Panthers
87. Vice-president of President Johnson (*abbr.*)
88. "This is the week I earn my salary"
92. Nuclear _____ Ban Treaty
94. Home state of President Johnson
95. Capital of West Germany
99. U.S. spy agency (*abbr.*)
100. The _____ Frontier

50. The 1960's

51. THE 1970'S

ACROSS:

5. Internal Revenue Service (*abbr.*)
7. Egyptian president
9. Middle East oil organization (*abbr.*)
11. Location of Vietnam massacre
13. 1972 candidate paralyzed by a would-be assassin
15. First president to visit Communist China
16. U.S. missile
19. Israeli Prime Minister
20. Home state of Senator Baker (*abbr.*)
21. Federal tax agency (*abbr.*)
22. Arab terrorists (*abbr.*)
23. Home state of President Carter (*abbr.*)
24. Country that seized American hostages
25. President who pardoned former President Nixon
26. Home state of President Ford (*abbr.*)
27. Nixon re-election campaign
31. Watergate investigator
33. Signed the Camp David Accords

34. President who resigned
35. Chief Justice of the Supreme Court
37. Number of terms for President Carter
38. Vice-president of President Carter
41. Soviet leader
42. Vice-president of President Nixon
44. Central Intelligence Agency (*abbr.*)
45. Home state of President Carter (*abbr.*)
46. Pentagon Papers informer
47. "Western White House"
50. Home state of vice-president Agnew (*abbr.*)
51. U.S. ship captured by Cambodia
56. Muslim ruler of Iran
57. Country invaded by the Soviet Union
58. Signed the Camp David Accords
59. "I will never lie to you"
60. President who returned the Canal Zone to Panama

DOWN:

1. U.S. spacecraft to Mars
2. Home state of Senator Ervin (*abbr.*)
3. Home state of George Wallace (*abbr.*)
4. President Nixon's Secretary of State
6. Peace talks with the Soviet Union (*abbr.*)
8. Vice-president of Richard Nixon
10. Embarrassing articles about Vietnam (*two words*)
11. U.S. missile
12. Location of Egyptian-Israeli peace agreement (*two words*)
14. America's two-hundredth birthday
17. Watergate investigator
18. Federal police (*abbr.*)
25. Federal Bureau of Investigation (*abbr.*)
27. U.S. spy agency (*abbr.*)
28. White House burglars
29. Nixon scandal

30. Vice-president who resigned
32. Home state of President Ford (*abbr.*)
36. Easing of political tensions
38. Democratic candidate in 1972
39. Home state of Senator Ervin (*abbr.*)
40. Intercontinental ballistic missile (*abbr.*)
43. War fought in the 1970's
48. President who held Egyptian-Israeli peace talks
49. Location of 1972 Republican national convention
50. Location of most Cuban immigrants
52. Home state of President Carter (*abbr.*)
53. Watergate investigator
54. Palestinian Liberation Front (*abbr.*)
55. Agreement to limit missiles in the U.S. and Soviet Union (*abbr.*)

51. The 1970's

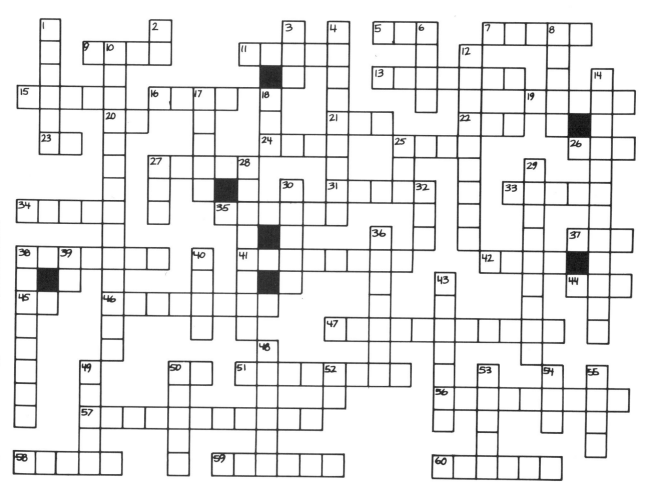

52. THE 1980's

© 1993 by The Center for Applied Research in Education

ACROSS:

3. Soviet leader
6. *Columbia* astronaut
7. Black candidate during the 1980's
10. First space shuttle
12. Island disputed between Britain and Argentina
13. Olympics boycotted by the United States
15. Communist island in the Caribbean Sea
17. Muslim terrorists (*abbr.*)
19. Nation divided between Christians and Muslims
21. Nation that captured U.S. hostages
24. First space shuttle pilot
25. President of Iraq
27. *Columbia* astronaut
28. Location of President Reagan's attempted assassination (*abbr.*)
29. War fought in 1982
30. 1980's president
32. Supreme Court Justice replaced by Sandra Day O'Connor
35. Soviet leader
38. Equal Rights Amendment (*abbr.*)
40. Nation invaded by U.S. troops on October 25, 1983
42. "Shoot from the hip"
43. Female vice-presidential candidate
45. _____ Air Force Base
47. Loser of the Falkland War
49. Home state of President Reagan (*abbr.*)
53. British Prime Minister
54. U.S. embassy bombed in Lebanon

DOWN:

1. Communist supplier of Grenada rebels
2. Peace-keeping organization (*abbr.*)
4. Residence of President Reagan (*abbr.*)
5. President when Iran hostages were freed
8. Soviet leader
9. Palestine Liberation Organization (*abbr.*)
11. First black astronaut
14. Location of Edwards Air Force Base (*abbr.*)
16. First shuttle pilot
18. Vice-president of President Carter
20. Vice-president of President Reagan
22. Space shuttle
23. Women's rights amendment (*abbr.*)
25. Would-be assassin of President Reagan
26. Central American nation involved in war
31. Soviet leader
33. Air force base for space shuttle landings
34. Number of terms for President Reagan
36. Iraq leader who invaded Iran
37. Assassinated leader of El Salvador
39. Winner of the Reagan-Carter TV debates
41. Nation that invaded Afghanistan (*abbr.*)
44. Hotel where President Reagan was shot
46. First female astronaut
48. Home state of Sandra Day O'Connor (*abbr.*)
50. Residence of President Reagan (*abbr.*)
51. District of Columbia (*abbr.*)
52. 1988 Republican candidate

52. The 1980's

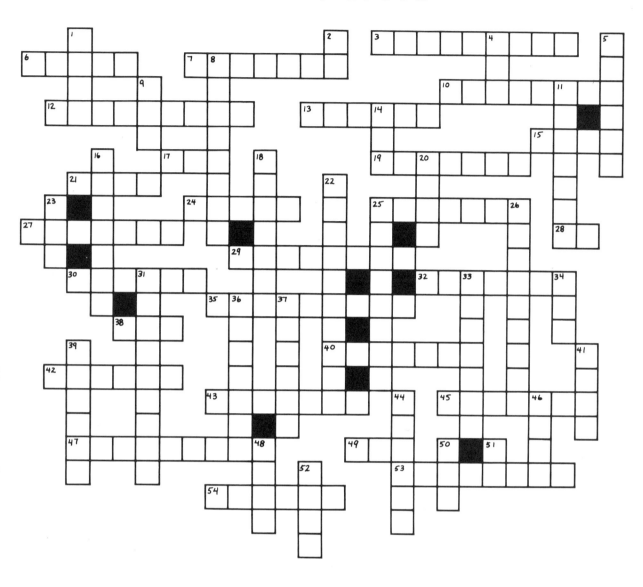

53. CAPITAL CITIES OF THE UNITED STATES

ACROSS:

1. Capital of Minnesota
4. Capital of Oregon
5. Capital of North Carolina
10. Capital of Vermont
11. Capital of Texas
12. Capital of Wisconsin
16. Capital of Utah
18. Capital of California
22. Capital of Indiana
24. Capital of Massachusetts
25. Capital of Virginia
26. _____ Moines, Iowa
28. Capital of Georgia
29. Capital of Louisiana
31. Capital of Colorado
32. Capital of Oregon
33. Capital of Washington
35. Capital of Ohio
37. Capital of Illinois

39. Santa _____, New Mexico
40. Capital of Alaska
41. Capital of Idaho
42. Capital of Kansas
43. Capital of Alaska
44. Capital of Montana
49. Capital of Connecticut
50. _____ Paul, Minnesota
51. Capital of Kentucky
53. Capital of New Hampshire
55. Capital of Texas
56. Capital of Idaho
58. Capital of New Mexico
60. Capital of Wyoming
61. Capital of South Carolina
62. Jefferson _____, Missouri
63. Capital of Rhode Island
64. Capital of West Virginia

DOWN:

2. Capital of Maine
3. Capital of New York
4. _____ Fe, New Mexico
6. Carson _____, Nevada
7. Capital of New Jersey
8. Capital of Nevada
9. Capital of Minnesota
13. Capital of Oklahoma
14. Capital of Pennsylvania
15. Capital of Nebraska
17. Capital of Alabama
19. Capital of Florida
20. Capital of North Dakota
21. Capital of West Virginia
23. Capital of Maryland
26. Capital of Iowa

27. Oklahoma _____, Oklahoma
30. Capital of Hawaii
34. Capital of Missouri
36. Capital of Arkansas
38. Capital of Delaware
43. Capital of Mississippi
45. Capital of Tennessee
47. Capital of Arizona
48. Capital of Michigan
52. Capital of South Dakota
54. Capital of Wisconsin
57. Little _____, Arkansas
58. _____ Lake City, Utah
59. Capital of Colorado
60. Salt Lake _____, Utah

Name _____ Date _____

53. Capital Cities of the United States

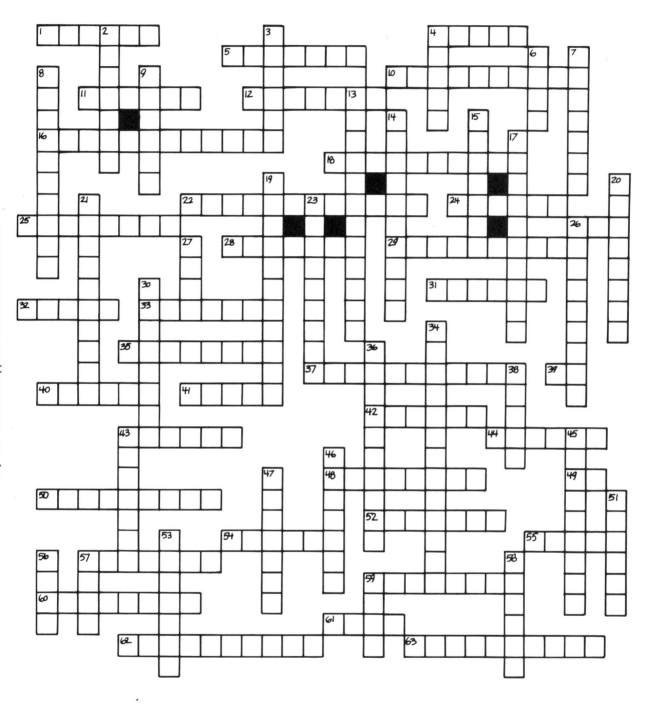

54. MOUNTAINS AND RIVERS OF THE UNITED STATES

ACROSS: _____

5. River of Virginia and North Carolina
6. River of southern Montana
8. River of Indiana
9. River dividing West Virginia and Ohio
10. River of Illinois
11. Mountain range of western Virginia
12. River dividing Minnesota and North Dakota
15. River of Pennsylvania
16. River of Idaho
18. River of New York
23. Eastern mountain range
26. Small "mountains" of southwestern South Dakota
28. Mountains of eastern California
29. River of Virginia
31. River dividing Texas and Mexico
35. River named after an English king
36. River dividing Georgia and Alabama

38. River flowing from North Dakota to Missouri
42. Largest river in the United States
43. River of Tennessee
44. Big _____ River
46. River of Washington, Oregon, and Idaho
49. Mountains of western Virginia and North Carolina
51. River of Montana
53. River of Nebraska
54. River boundary with Mexico before the Gadsden Purchase
56. River separating New Jersey and Pennsylvania
58. Mountains of western Maine
59. River of New Mexico and Texas
60. River of Wyoming and Montana
61. River separating Maine and Canada
62. River of Alaska

DOWN: _____

1. River separating Texas and Louisiana
2. River dividing Texas and Oklahoma
3. River of Alaska
4. River dividing Idaho and Utah
6. Mountains of northeastern Oregon
7. River of Alaska
8. Mountains of New Hampshire
11. River of Idaho
12. River separating Texas and Oklahoma
13. Mountains extending from Washington to California
14. River dividing Kentucky and Ohio
16. River dividing South Carolina and Georgia
17. Mountains of southeastern New York
19. Mountains of Arkansas
20. River flowing through the Grand Canyon
21. River of California
22. River dividing Kentucky and Indiana
24. Mountains of northeastern New York
25. River separating Oregon and Idaho
26. River of central Texas

27. River of California
30. River dividing Oregon and Washington
32. Western mountain range
33. Mountains of eastern Tennessee
34. River of Arkansas
35. River of eastern South Dakota
37. Mountains of California, Oregon, and Washington
39. River separating Kentucky and Indiana
40. River of southern Arizona
41. River separating Idaho and Washington
45. River of western Pennsylvania
47. River separating Virginia and Maryland
48. River separating Minnesota and South Dakota
49. River of Texas
50. Mountains of Vermont
52. River of southern Texas
53. River of New Mexico
55. River of Texas
57. _____ Grande River

54. Mountains and Rivers of the United States

55. STATE FLOWERS

ACROSS:

4. State flower of Arizona: blossom of
   _____ cactus
5. State flower of Ohio: scarlet _____
10. State flower of Tennessee
12. State flower of Louisiana
14. State flower of Arkansas
18. Blossom of _____ cactus
20. State flower of Virginia
23. State flower of Connecticut: mountain
    _____
24. State flower of Kansas: native _____
28. State flower of Montana
30. State flower of New York
31. Forget-_____-not
32. State flower of Iowa: wild _____
33. State flower of Hawaii: yellow _____
34. State flower of New York and Iowa
36. State flower of North Dakota: wild
    prairie _____

37. Wild _____
39. State flower of West Virginia: big _____
40. State flower of Alabama
41. State flower of Oklahoma
45. State flower of Michigan
48. State flower of New Jersey: purple
    _____
49. State flower of Wisconsin: wood _____
50. Forget-me-_____
51. State flower of New Mexico
54. State flower of Rhode Island
55. State flower of Washington: western
    _____
56. State flower of Iowa: wild _____
57. State flower of Arkansas
58. State flower of North Carolina
59. State flower of New York

DOWN:

1. State flower of Pennsylvania: mountain
   _____
2. State flower of Tennessee
3. State flower of Alabama
6. State flower of Iowa: wild _____
7. State flower of Tennessee
8. State flower of Kentucky
9. State flower of Massachusetts
11. State flower of Alaska
13. State flower of Nebraska
15. State flower of Connecticut and
    Pennsylvania: mountain _____
16. State flower of Minnesota: pink and
    white _____
17. State flower of North Carolina and
    Virginia
19. State flower of Florida

21. State flower of Delaware
22. State flower of Illinois: native _____
25. State flower of Missouri
26. State flower of Texas
27. State flower of Vermont: red _____
29. State flower of Tennessee
35. State flower of Delaware
38. State flower of Nevada
42. State flower of New York
43. State flower of Mississippi
44. State flower of Iowa: wild _____
46. State flower of Virginia
47. State flower of North Carolina
52. State flower of Virginia
53. State flower of New Jersey and Rhode
    Island

55. State Flowers

Flowering dogwood

56. STATE BIRDS

ACROSS: _____

2. State bird of South Dakota
5. State bird of Kentucky
9. State bird of Minnesota: common _____
10. State bird of California
13. State bird of Connecticut: American _____
14. State bird of Maryland
15. State bird of South Dakota
19. State bird of Hawaii: Nene _____
20. State bird of Michigan
22. State bird of Kansas: Western _____
23. State bird of West Virginia
25. State bird of New Mexico

29. State bird of Utah
30. State bird of Idaho: mountain _____
32. State bird of Minnesota: common _____
34. State bird of Maine
35. State bird of Maryland
36. State bird of Montana: Western _____
37. State bird of Virginia
38. State bird of Arkansas
42. State bird of Florida
44. State bird of Missouri
46. State bird of North Carolina
48. State bird of Oregon: Western _____
49. State bird of New Jersey: Eastern _____

DOWN: _____

1. State bird of Texas
2. State bird of Louisiana: Eastern brown _____
3. State bird of Tennessee
4. State bird of Minnesota: common _____
6. State bird of Arizona
7. State bird of Maine
8. State bird of Washington: willow _____
11. State bird of Minnesota: common _____
12. State bird of Wyoming
16. State bird of Ohio
17. State bird of Wisconsin
18. State bird of North Dakota: Western _____

21. State bird of Iowa
24. State bird of Nebraska
26. State bird of Hawaii: Nene _____
27. State bird of New York
28. State bird of Maryland
31. State bird of Nevada: mountain _____
33. State bird of Mississippi
39. State bird of Pennsylvania: ruffed _____
40. State bird of California
43. State bird of Maryland
47. State bird of Minnesota: common _____

56. State Birds

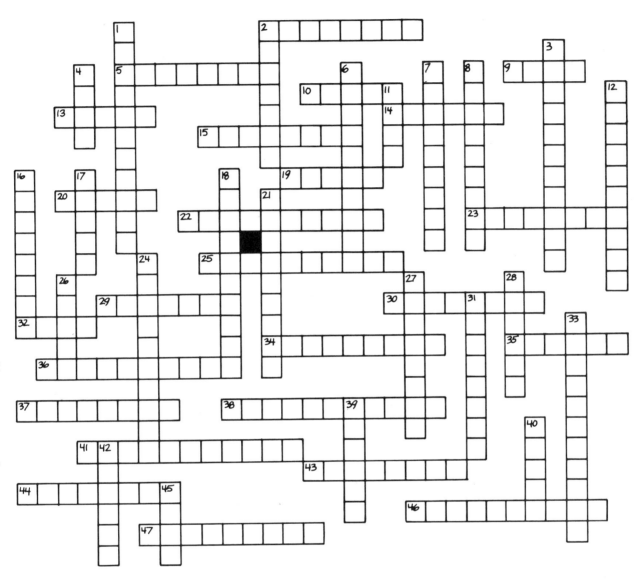

57. STATE NICKNAMES

ACROSS:

1. Hoosier State
8. Old Dominion
10. Mountain State
12. Land of Opportunity
16. Free State
17. Evergreen State
19. Bay State
21. Prairie State
22. Sooner State
24. Wolverine State
26. Silver State (or Sagebrush State)
27. Hawkeye State
28. Golden State
29. Land of Enchantment
30. Gem State
31. Lone Star State
33. Treasure State
35. Gopher State (or North Star State)
36. Sunflower State
38. Centennial State
39. Beaver State
40. Aloha State
43. First State
44. Granite State
45. Ocean State
46. Empire State
47. Cornhusker State

DOWN:

2. Hawkeye State
3. Green Mountain State
4. Buckeye State
5. Beehive State
6. Grand Canyon State
7. Show-Me State
9. Heart of Dixie
11. Palmetto State
13. Empire State
14. Keystone State
15. Pine Tree State
18. Constitution State (or Nutmeg State)
20. Volunteer State
21. Hawkeye State
23. Pelican State
24. Magnolia State
25. Sunflower State
32. Peach State
34. Sunshine State
37. Garden State
39. Beaver State
41. Last Frontier
42. Buckeye State

57. State Nicknames

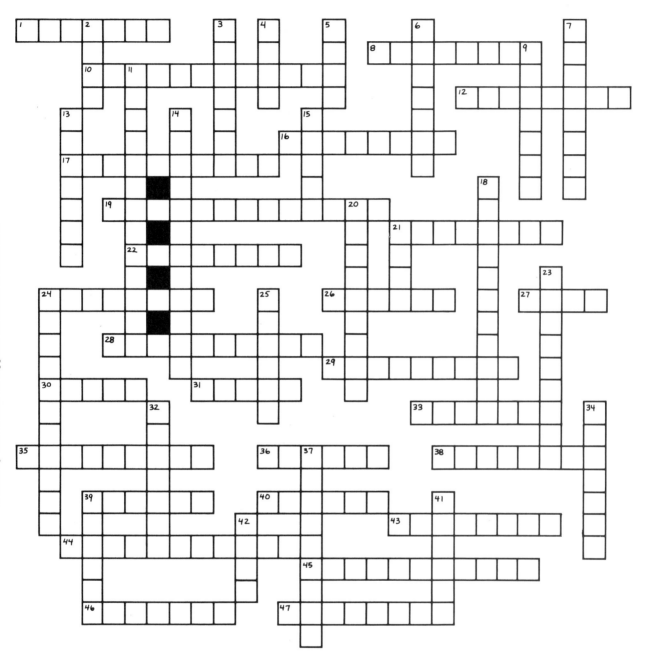

58. PRESIDENTIAL TRIVIA

ACROSS:

2. Only president married while in office
9. Second president to die in office
10. Introduced handshaking to replace the bow at White House receptions
11. First president to have been divorced
13. Oldest man elected to the presidency
14. Youngest man to serve as president
16. Smallest president (5'4")
17. First president whose state of residence was west of the Mississippi River
21. Second president to die in office
22. Last president born in the 19th century
24. Lived longer than any other president
26. First president to be photographed while in office
27. Youngest man ever elected president
29. Only president to become a member of the Confederate Congress
32. First president born outside the original thirteen states
33. First president to be impeached
36. Only president inaugurated in New York City
37. Only president to have a son elected president
41. First president to ride on a railroad train
43. First president to travel abroad

44. First president born in a log cabin
45. First president to die in office
49. Only bachelor president
51. First president to wear trousers instead of breeches
54. Second president to be assassinated
55. Only president to have been shot and wounded in office and recovered
56. First president defeated for re-election
57. President when the stock market crashed to begin the Great Depression
60. Only president to have been Speaker of the House
61. Only president to serve in the Senate after leaving office
62. Only president to serve as Chief Justice of the Supreme Court
69. Served the shortest term of any president
71. Only president to have killed a man in a duel
72. Only president to earn a Ph.D. degree
73. Last president born in the 18th century
74. Only president born on the Fourth of July
76. First president to resign
77. First president to visit Europe
78. First president to ride in an automobile

DOWN:

1. Died on July 4
2. Only president born in a hospital
3. First president born west of the Rockies
4. Died on July 4
5. First Roman Catholic president
6. First president whose veto was overridden
7. Lived longer after leaving office than any other president
8. Fourth president to be assassinated
9. Heaviest president (over 300 pounds)
11. First president born west of the Mississippi River
12. First president to win the Nobel Peace Prize
15. First president to visit Communist China
18. First president to be assassinated
19. First president to have been a movie actor
20. Only president unanimously elected
21. One of only two presidents buried in Arlington Cemetery
23. Only president to serve two nonconsecutive terms
25. One of only two presidents buried in Arlington Cemetery
28. First president to appear on color television
30. President who had polio
31. President when U.S. landed on the moon
33. First president on whom an assassination attempt was made
34. Only president to serve in the House of Representatives after leaving office

35. President during the War of 1812
38. First president born in the 20th century
39. First president elected while a resident of a state other than his native state
40. Only president who did not live in Washington, D.C.
42. First president to appear on television
46. President who appointed a woman to the Supreme Court
47. First president to speak over the radio
48. President who made the Gadsden Purchase
49. This president's dog, Millie, "wrote" a best-selling book
50. Sixth president to die in office
52. First president to visit the Soviet Union during peacetime
53. First president who had not served in Congress
58. President during the Falkland Islands War
59. Only president sworn into office by his father
63. President who was not elected
64. Tallest president (6'4")
65. Last president with a beard
67. First president sworn in by a woman
68. First president whose inauguration was reported by telegraph
70. Only president who was a published poet
75. President during the Mexican War

58. Presidential Trivia

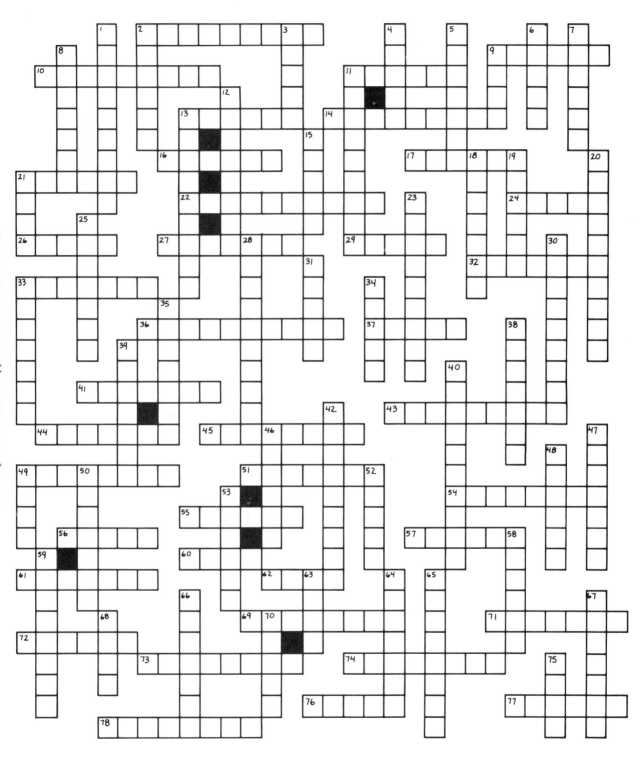

Name _____ Date _____

59. PRESIDENTIAL QUOTATIONS

ACROSS:

6. "Shoot from the hip"
7. "All men are created equal"
9. "Steer clear of permanent alliances"
12. "Speak softly and carry a big stick"
16. "First in war, first in peace, and first in the hearts of his countrymen"
18. "War on poverty"
19. "A date which will live in infamy"

22. "I am not a crook"
23. "The buck stops here"
24. "Fifty-four, forty, or fight"
25. "Those who labor in the earth are chosen people of God"
27. "Four score and seven years ago"
28. "We must make the world safe for democracy"

DOWN:

1. "I'm tired of babying the Soviets"
2. "A house divided against itself cannot stand"
3. "I cannot tell a lie"
4. "I will never lie to you"
5. "This is the week I earn my salary"
8. "If you can't stand the heat, get out of the kitchen"
11. "Ask not what your country can do for you, ask what you can do for your country"

13. "I could do nothing else and still be president"
14. "I'm strong as a bull moose and you may use me to the limit"
15. "The business of America is business"
17. "Return to normalcy"
20. "With malice toward none, with charity for all"
21. "Millions for defense, but not one cent for tribute"
26. "For every American, this has to be the proudest day of our lives"

© 1993 by The Center for Applied Research in Education

Name _____ Date _____

60. PRESIDENTIAL NICKNAMES

ACROSS: _____

3. "His Rotundity"
4. "Old Hickory"
7. "The Butcher"
9. "Old Tippecanoe"
12. "Unconditional Surrender"
13. "Teddy"

16. "Ike"
21. "Honest Abe"
22. "Jimmy"
24. "Andy Jackson in a jetliner"
25. "The Little Magician"

DOWN: _____

1. "The father of our country"
2. FDR
5. "Silent Cal"
6. "Father of the Constitution"
8. "Long Tom"
10. "Uncle Jumbo"
11. "Old Rough and Ready"

14. JFK
15. LBJ
17. "Old Buck"
18. "The pacifist professor"
19. "The front porch campaigner"
20. "Jerry"
23. "Old man eloquent"

61. PRESIDENTIAL BIRTHPLACES

ACROSS: _____

7. Birthplace of Presidents Roosevelt and Fillmore
10. Birthplace of President Jackson
11. Birthplace of President Buchanan
13. Birthplace of Presidents Grant and Garfield
14. Birthplace of Presidents Washington and Jefferson

17. Birthplace of Presidents Eisenhower and L. Johnson
18. Birthplace of Presidents Madison and Monroe
19. Birthplace of President Ford
20. Birthplace of President Cleveland

DOWN: _____

1. Birthplace of President Nixon
2. Birthplace of President Hoover
3. Birthplace of Presidents Arthur and Coolidge
4. Birthplace of President Pierce
5. Birthplace of Presidents Polk and A. Johnson
6. Birthplace of President Lincoln

8. Birthplace of Presidents Kennedy and Bush
9. Birthplace of President Truman
12. Birthplace of President Carter
15. Birthplace of President Reagan
16. Birthplace of Presidents Harding and Harrison

Name _____   Date _____

62. VICE PRESIDENTS

ACROSS:

2. Vice president who resigned over tax evasion

4. Sixth vice president to become president upon the death of his predecessor

6. First vice president

8. First vice president to become president upon the resignation of his predecessor

9. Vice president who pardoned Richard Nixon after becoming president

10. First vice president to become president upon the assassination of his predecessor

11. Fourth vice president to become president upon the assassination of his predecessor

12. First vice president to become president upon the death of his predecessor

DOWN:

1. Third vice president to become president upon the assassination of his predecessor

3. First vice president to participate in a televised debate

5. Second vice president to become president upon the death of his predecessor

6. First vice president to be elected president

7. Second vice president to become president upon the assassination of his predecessor

63. ADMINISTRATION NICKNAMES

ACROSS: _____

1. Administration of Theodore Roosevelt
3. Administration of John F. Kennedy
4. Administration of Lyndon B. Johnson
5. Administration of Harry S. Truman

6. Administration of Franklin D. Roosevelt
7. Administration of Warren G. Harding
8. Administration of Lyndon B. Johnson

DOWN: _____

2. Administration of James Monroe

Name _____ Date _____

64. WARTIME PRESIDENTS

ACROSS: _____

3. President during the Spanish-American War

4. President at the beginning of the Vietnam War

8. President at the beginning of World War II

9. President at the end of World War II

10. President during the Vietnam War

DOWN: _____

1. President during the Mexican War

2. President during the Civil War

3. President during the War of 1812

5. President during World War I

6. President at the end of the Vietnam War

7. President during the Persian Gulf War

65. LOSING PRESIDENTIAL CANDIDATES

ACROSS: ————————————————————————

2. Constitutional Union candidate in 1860
4. American Independent candidate in 1968
8. Democratic candidate in 1848
10. First vice president to lose an election for president
15. Republican candidate in 1916
17. Democratic candidate in 1876
18. Democratic candidate in 1972
19. Whig candidate in 1844

20. Bull Moose candidate in 1912
21. Democratic candidate in 1980
22. Democratic candidate in 1920
25. Democratic candidate in 1896
26. Republican candidate in 1960
27. Democratic candidate in 1904
28. Republican candidate in 1976
29. Democratic candidate in 1860
30. Democratic candidate in 1900

DOWN: ————————————————————————

1. Republican candidate in 1884
3. Democratic candidate in 1840
5. Independent candidate in 1980
6. Republican candidate in 1936
7. Democratic candidate in 1888
9. Whig candidate in 1852
11. Democratic candidate in 1952 and 1956

12. Republican candidate in 1948
13. Democratic candidate in 1928
14. Democratic candidate in 1868
16. Republican candidate in 1964
23. Republican candidate in 1916
24. Republican candidate in 1832
25. Democratic candidate in 1908

Name _____   Date _____

66. FIRST LADIES

ACROSS: _____

4. First Lady of Dwight D. Eisenhower
6. First Lady of John Adams
8. First Lady of Gerald R. Ford
9. First Lady of Andrew Jackson
10. First Lady of Richard M. Nixon

11. First Lady of Harry S. Truman
13. First Lady of Abraham Lincoln
14. First Lady of James Madison
15. First Lady of Ronald Reagan

DOWN: _____

1. First Lady of George Washington
2. First Lady of Lyndon B. Johnson
3. First Lady of John F. Kennedy
5. First Lady of Franklin D. Roosevelt

7. First Lady of Bill Clinton
9. First Lady of Jimmy Carter
12. First Lady of Rutherford B. Hayes

67. CHIEF JUSTICES OF THE SUPREME COURT

ACROSS: _____

3. Famous Chief Justice who served over thirty years

5. Chief Justice during the Dred Scott decision

6. Chief Justice during Andrew Johnson's impeachment trial

DOWN: _____

1. Chief Justice during the Brown v. Board of Education decision

2. Only president to serve as Chief Justice

4. First Chief Justice

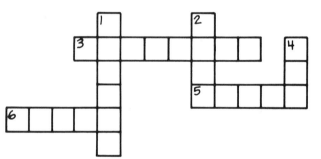

Name _____ Date _____

68. DEATHS AND ASSASSINATIONS

ACROSS:

1. Assassinated in Dallas, Texas by Lee Harvey Oswald
5. Assassinated by Charles Guiteau
6. Third president to be assassinated

7. Died shortly after his inauguration
9. Died while serving in his fourth term
11. Died on the Fourth of July

DOWN:

1. Civil rights leader assassinated by James Earl Ray
2. Assassinated by John Wilkes Booth
3. Died on the Fourth of July
4. Presidential candidate assassinated by Sirhan Sirhan

7. Died of a heart attack on August 2, 1923
8. Died on the Fourth of July
10. Died suddenly on July 9, 1850

69. AMERICAN MILITARY LEADERS

ACROSS: _____

3. Union naval leader at New Orleans
10. Naval leader in World War II
11. Fighter at the Alamo
12. Confederate general
13. Calvary leader at Little Big Horn
16. "Old Fuss and Feathers"
17. Naval leader in the War of 1812
18. Army leader in the War of 1812
19. "Old Tippecanoe"
26. Leader in the Pacific in World War II
27. Leader in Europe in World War II
28. Union general

30. "We have met the enemy and they are ours"
31. Leader in the Vietnam War
32. Leader in the American Revolution
35. Supreme Allied Commander in World War II
39. Leader in World War II
40. Leader in the Korean War
43. Union general
45. Leader in the Mexican War
47. Leader of Tokyo bombing raids in World War II
48. Leader in North Africa during World War II

DOWN: _____

1. Leader in the War of 1812 at New Orleans
2. Leader in the Revolutionary War at Saratoga
4. "Old Rough and Ready"
5. Leader in the Mexican War
6. Known for his "March to the Sea"
7. Confederate leader at Gettysburg
8. Naval leader in the Spanish-American War
9. Confederate leader "Stonewall"
14. Famous calvary scout
15. "The Butcher"
20. "Damn the torpedoes, full steam ahead"
21. Confederate leader at Appomattox
22. Revolutionary War leader
23. Mexican War general "The Long Marcher"
24. Union general at Gettysburg

25. Army leader pursuing Pancho Villa
26. Revolutionary War leader
28. Mexican War general
29. Union general
31. Leader in the French and Indian War
33. "Unconditional Surrender"
34. Naval leader in World War II
36. Mexican War leader and Texas president
37. Fighter at the Alamo
38. Union general at Appomattox
41. "The Swamp Fox"
42. Spanish-American War leader at Puerto Rico
44. "Stormin'" _____ Schwarzkopf of the Persian Gulf War
46. Confederate general

Name _____ Date _____

69. American Military Leaders

Name _____ Date _____

70. AMERICANS IN SPACE

ACROSS: _____

1. One-man spacecraft
4. Location of space shuttle landings (*abbr.*)
7. Air Force base where the space shuttle lands
8. Location of the space control center
10. First astronaut to orbit the Earth
11. First astronaut on the moon
12. Lunar landing craft
13. Location of space launchings (*two words*)
16. First astronaut in space
18. First black astronaut
20. Two-man spacecraft
21. First American satellite

DOWN: _____

2. Space shuttle that exploded seconds after takeoff
3. First female astronaut
5. Three-man spacecraft
6. First space shuttle
9. Reusable spacecraft
13. Astronaut killed in an *Apollo* fire
14. Second astronaut on the moon
15. Location of Cape Canaveral (*abbr.*)
17. Astronaut killed in an *Apollo* fire
19. Location of Houston Control Center (*abbr.*)

Name ———————————————— Date ————————————

70. Americans in Space

Name ——————————————————————   Date ——————————————

71. WOMEN IN AMERICAN HISTORY

ACROSS:

4. An early traveler through New England
7. "Molly Pitcher"
9. Author of *Uncle Tom's Cabin*
10. Suffragette
12. "Calamity Jane"
13. Appointed sergeant in the Revolutionary Army by George Washington
14. Author of *Seven Financial Conspiracies*
15. Author of *History of the Standard Oil Company*
17. Abolitionist
18. Founded the Locust Street Social Settlement for blacks
19. Elected to the House of Representatives in 1916
20. Abolitionist sisters
24. Populist leader
26. Banned from Boston for religious discussions
28. Author of *The Homemaker* in 1924

30. 1920's singer and dancer
31. Mother of Abraham Lincoln
33. Labor organizer and "mother"
34. Editor of *Vanity Fair*
37. Montana congresswoman
38. Author of *Silent Spring*
40. One of the founders of the Women's Party
42. Started a school in Washington, D.C. to train black teachers
43. One of the founders of the Women's Party
44. Founder of Mount Holyoke Female Seminary
45. Designer of women's "bloomers"
50. Union spy in the Civil War
54. First woman to receive a degree in medicine
56. Author of *The Feminine Mystique*
57. Started public hospitals for the insane
59. Famous athlete of the 1930's
61. First child born in the British colonies in America (last name)

DOWN:

1. Author of *Coming of Age in Samoa*
2. President of the National American Woman Suffrage Association
3. Publisher of women's rights newspaper "The Lily"
5. Heroine of the Battle of Monmouth in the American Revolution
6. Lawyer in the Mullen v. Oregon case to limit working hours
8. Attended the World's Antislavery Convention in London
9. One of the founders of Hull House in Chicago
11. Executed for espionage in 1953
13. Banned from Massachusetts and killed by Indians
16. French actress who toured America in the 1880's
18. Member of Roosevelt's "black cabinet" and college founder
21. Author of *Gone With the Wind*
22. Nation's first woman cabinet member
23. An early traveler through New England
25. "Conductor" on the "underground railroad"
27. First woman justice on the Supreme Court
28. Author of *The Homemaker*

29. Montana congresswoman
32. 1920's actress, singer, and dancer
33. Author of *A Century of Dishonor*
35. Female aviator lost in 1937
36. Revolutionary War female soldier
39. Suffragette
41. Witness of Andrew Jackson's inauguration party
46. Vigorous member of the Populist Party
47. Ambassador to Italy during Eisenhower's administration
48. Organizer of the International Ladies Garment Workers' Union
49. Lawyer in the Mullen v. Oregon case to limit working hours
51. Improved treatment for the mentally insane
52. Populist leader
53. Refused to sit in the back of a bus in Alabama
55. Opened the first women's college in Massachusetts
58. Founder of Henry Street Settlement House in New York
60. Responsible for St. Elizabeth's Hospital for the insane

Name _____   Date _____

71. Women in American History

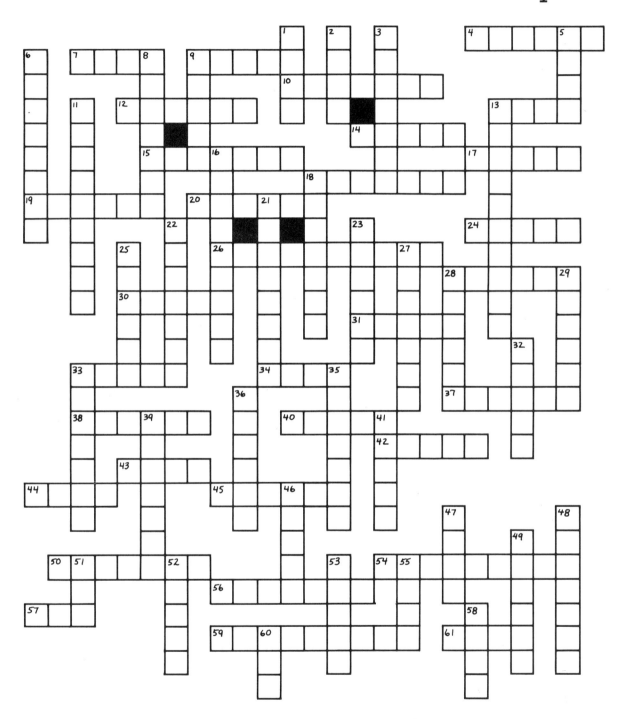

© 1993 by The Center for Applied Research in Education

Name _____   Date _____

72. AMERICAN ATHLETES

ACROSS:

4. Baseball's "Say-Hey Kid"
6. Tennis's "Big Bill"
8. Golfer with an "army"
12. Baseball's "Pee wee"
13. Boxer "Smokin' Joe"
14. "The Yankee Clipper"
16. "The Babe"

20. Golfer "Slammin' Sammy"
21. Jockey "The Shoe"
22. Football's "The Galloping Ghost"
23. Baseball's "Charlie Hustle"
24. Winner of the "Grand Slam"
25. "The Manassa Mauler"

DOWN:

1. Baseball's "The Mick"
2. Boxer Ali as an amateur
3. Female tennis star
5. Baseball's "Ironman"
7. 1930's female sports star
9. Baseball's "Dizzy"
10. Cassius Clay

11. Archrival of boxer Mohammed Ali
15. Track star of the Berlin Olympics
16. Baseball's leading hit-getter
17. Famous Indian athlete
18. Baseball's all-time homerun leader
19. Baseball's single-season homerun leader

ATHLETICS

Name _____ Date _____

73. AMERICAN ENTERTAINERS

ACROSS: _____

4. Comedian with wife Gracie Allen
5. Comedian famous for his Christmas trips

7. "The Toast of the Town" host
9. Trick lariat twirler; cowboy philosopher
10. "Mr. Television"

DOWN: _____

1. Cartoon animator
2. Wild West Show owner
3. Vaudeville star in the first "talkie"

6. 1950's–60's rock-and-roll singer
8. Three-ring circus manager

Name _____ Date _____

74. QUOTATIONS IN AMERICAN HISTORY

ACROSS:

2. "What you farmers need to do is raise less corn and more hell"
4. "What hath God wrought"
7. "War is hell"
9. "I shall return"
11. "You shall not crucify mankind on a cross of gold"

12. "I have a dream"
13. "Well, I have been and gone and done it"
15. "There's a sucker born every minute"
16. "Watson, come in here"
17. "Plant a tree, a shrub, or a bush"
18. "Give the lady what she wants"

DOWN:

1. "I never met a man I didn't like"
3. "To realize what war is, one should follow in our tracks"
5. "No work, no eat"
6. "We have met the enemy and they are ours"
8. "Old soldiers never die, they just fade away"

10. "One small step for man, one giant leap for mankind"
12. "It was a great ride"
14. "You may fire when ready, Gridley"
15. "Sic semper tyrannus"

75. AMERICAN NICKNAMES

ACROSS: _____

5. "The Flying Fool"
8. "The Moses of her People"
12. "Calamity Jane"
13. "Uncle Joe"
15. "Wild Bill"
17. "The Manassa Mauler"

19. "Boy orator of the Platte"
20. "The Great Compromiser"
21. "Fighting Bob"
24. "The Swamp Fox"
25. "The Long Marcher"
26. "The Wizard of Menlo Park"

DOWN: _____

1. "Black Jack"
2. "Billy the Kid"
3. "Buffalo Bill"
4. "The Babe"
6. "Fighting Joe"
7. "Stonewall"
9. "Tardy George"

10. "Deadwood Dick"
11. "Gentleman Jim"
14. "Mad Anthony"
16. "The Galloping Ghost"
18. "Old Fuss and Feathers"
22. "The Kingfish"
23. "Molly Pitcher"

Name _____   Date _____

76. -ISMS

ACROSS:

2. System by which a nation maintains foreign colonies for profit
4. Belief that the value of an idea is whether or not it works
6. Belief that material goods and wealth are the most important values in life
10. Belief that a nation should remain free of international alliances
12. System of government characterized by an absolute dictator
13. Recording of news events on film
18. Practice of favoring native-born Americans
19. Use of two metals as a monetary standard
20. Associating workers to promote and protect their interests
21. Favoring Americans and restricting immigrants
22. Placing the interests of one region ahead of the welfare of the whole nation

DOWN:

1. Political system in which the government controls the means of production
3. Excessive emphasis on aggressive attitudes and military spirit
4. Rejecting the use of force, violence, or war
5. Feelings of loyalty, pride, and devotion to one's country
7. Economic theory that promises a nation power through a favorable balance of trade
8. Maintaining foreign colonies
9. Movement begun by farmers who wanted economic and political reform
10. Policy of a nation to acquire an empire by controlling weaker territories
11. Emphasis on war policies in national life and government
14. Economic system in which the means of production are privately owned
15. System of government in which the nation and the states share authority
16. Showing respect and pride in one's country
17. Economic system characterized by common ownership of property

77. FAMOUS AMERICAN NAMES BEGINNING WITH A

ACROSS: _____

1. Second president
4. Killed in the Boston Massacre
5. Author of *Do and Dare*
6. Abigail _____

8. Vice president who resigned in 1973
9. Union commander at Fort Sumter
11. Author of *Luck and Pluck*
12. Founder of Texas

DOWN: _____

2. Women's suffrage leader
3. Killed at the Battle of Little Big Horn: George _____ Custer
6. Sixth president

7. Founder of Hull House in Chicago
8. American traitor in the Revolutionary War
10. Twenty-first president

Name _____ Date _____

78. FAMOUS AMERICAN NAMES BEGINNING WITH B

ACROSS: _____

2. Secretary of State in the Confederate Cabinet
6. Killed Alexander Hamilton in a duel
7. Inventor of the telephone
8. Assassin of Abraham Lincoln
9. Founded the Locust Street Social Settlement House in Hampton, Virginia
10. Fifteenth president

12. Forty-first president
13. Jazz-Age performer
17. Kansas abolitionist
19. Preacher who gave "Bibles" to Kansas abolitionists
20. Author of "The Lily," a women's rights paper
21. President Grant's Secretary of War

DOWN: _____

1. President of the Bank of the United States
3. Led a Virginia farmers' rebellion in 1676
4. First woman to come to the colony of Virginia
5. Member of Roosevelt's "Black Cabinet" and a college founder
7. Gave the "Cross of Gold" speech
11. Washington, D.C. architect

12. Union general at Fredericksburg
14. Woodsman who built the Wilderness Road
15. French actress who toured America in the 1880's
16. Missouri senator who wanted to give away western lands
17. "Billy the Kid"
18. First woman to receive a medical degree

79. FAMOUS AMERICAN NAMES BEGINNING WITH C

ACROSS:

2. "The Great Compromiser"
3. "Calamity Jane"
5. Thirtieth president
7. U.S. calvary leader killed at Little Big Horn
10. Black Panther Leader
13. Mark Twain
14. Author of *The Red Badge of Courage*
18. "Peace and Freedom" presidential candidate in 1968

19. Andrew Jackson's vice president and South Carolina senator
20. Botanist at Tuskegee Institute
21. President of the National American Woman Suffrage Association
22. Steel industry millionaire and philanthropist
23. Leader of the Union Pacific railroad work gangs

DOWN:

1. Folk hero killed at the Alamo
2. "Buffalo Bill"
4. Twenty-second and twenty-fourth president
5. *Columbia* space shuttle pilot
6. Mexican-American migrant farmers' organizer
8. Abraham Lincoln's Secretary of Treasury

9. Explorer of the Louisiana Territory
11. Forty-second president
12. Thirty-ninth president
15. Famous Speaker of the House, "Uncle Joe"
16. Woman's suffragist
17. Famous boxer, "Gentleman Jim"
18. Watergate Special Prosecutor

80. FAMOUS AMERICAN NAMES BEGINNING WITH D

ACROSS: _____

2. Inventor of baseball
5. President of the Republic of Hawaii
6. "You may fire when ready, Gridley"
7. Inventor of the steel plow
10. "The British are coming"
11. Founder of the NAACP

13. Female athlete of the 1930's, "Babe"
14. Opponent of Harry S. Truman in 1948
15. Lawyer in the famous Scopes trial
16. President of the Confederate States of America
17. Famous boxer, "The Manassa Mauler"

DOWN: _____

1. President Eisenhower's Secretary of State
2. Nixon's aide involved with the Watergate scandal
3. Author of *Sister Carrie*
4. 1920's movie producer
5. Led the crusade to help the mentally insane
6. Author of *Letters from a Farmer in Pennsylvania to the Inhabitants of the British Colonies*

7. Led the Tokyo bombing raid during World War II
8. Chicago mayor during the 1968 Democratic Convention
9. Socialist Party presidential candidate in 1912 and 1920
11. Publisher of "The North Star"
12. Illinois senator who debated Abraham Lincoln

Name _____   Date _____

81. FAMOUS AMERICAN NAMES BEGINNING WITH E

ACROSS: _____

3. Famous inventor
5. Female aviator
7. Thirty-fourth president

8. Exposed the "Pentagon Papers"
9. Designed a steam engine in 1804
10. Female Union spy

DOWN: _____

1. Inventor of the Kodak camera
2. Refugee scientist from Hitler's Germany
3. Author of *Self-Reliance*
4. Nixon's aide involved with the Watergate scandal

5. Watergate investigator
6. Slain NAACP official
9. Author of *The Waste Land*

82. FAMOUS AMERICAN NAMES BEGINNING WITH F

ACROSS:

3. Organizer of the International Ladies Garment Workers' Union
6. Thirteenth president
7. First Grand Wizard of the Ku Klux Klan
9. Arkansas governor who tried to prevent school integration
10. Author of *This Side of Paradise*

12. Author of *Poor Richard's Almanack*
13. President Harding's Interior Secretary in the Teapot Dome scandal
14. Author of *The Great Gatsby*
15. Mexican War hero
16. Author of *The Feminine Mystique*
17. Inventor of the steamboat

DOWN:

1. Union naval leader
2. "Clermont" inventor
3. Thirty-eighth president
4. "Give the lady what she wants"
5. American composer
7. Founder of the National Organization of Women

8. Franklin D. Roosevelt's Postmaster General
11. "Damn the torpedoes, full steam ahead"
12. Inventor of the Model T
14. President who pardoned Richard Nixon

83. FAMOUS AMERICAN NAMES BEGINNING WITH G

ACROSS:

4. "The Galloping Ghost"
6. Founder of the American Federation of Labor
8. Antislavery spokeswoman
9. Editor of *The Liberator*
10. Inventor of barbed wire
11. Thomas Jefferson's Secretary of the Treasury
13. Director of the F.B.I. after J. Edgar Hoover
14. President Nixon's F.B.I. director
15. 1964 Republican presidential candidate
16. Assassin of President Garfield
18. Inventor of vulcanized rubber

DOWN:

1. Revolutionary War general at the battle of Saratoga
2. American astronaut
3. Tennessee war hawk prior to the War of 1812
4. Editor of the *New York Tribune* during Reconstruction
5. Twentieth president
6. Lawyer in the Muller v. Oregon labor case
7. Revolutionary War general in the Carolinas
9. First college football hero
11. Eighteenth president
12. Acting director of the F.B.I. in 1972
14. Tennessee war hawk
17. Vice president to Bill Clinton

Name ——————————————— Date ———————————

84. FAMOUS AMERICAN NAMES BEGINNING WITH H

ACROSS: _____

2. Republican presidential candidate in 1916
4. "Return to Normalcy" president
7. President when the Great Depression began
8. Theodore Roosevelt's Secretary of State
9. Campaign manager of President McKinley
10. Communist spy jailed after World War II
12. Boston theologian banned from Massachusetts
13. "Molly Pitcher"
16. Cowboy hero, "Wild Bill"
17. Vice president of Lyndon B. Johnson

19. Franklin Roosevelt's Secretary of State
21. Owner of the *New York Morning Journal*
22. Author of *The Sun Also Rises*
24. Killed while holding "the dead man's hand"
25. Democratic presidential candidate in 1984
26. U.S. ambassador to Moscow after World War II
27. "Give me liberty, or give me death"
28. Union commander at the battle of Chancellorsville

DOWN: _____

1. "God's in His Heaven, all's right with the world"
2. Twenty-ninth president
3. One of the leaders of the Antifederalists
5. President of the Republic of Texas
6. Supreme Court Justice in 1916
8. Chairman of the Second Continental Congress
10. Attempted assassin of President Reagan
11. Nineteenth president
14. Nixon's aide involved with the Watergate scandal

15. Nixon's aide involved with the Watergate scandal
16. President Washington's Secretary of the Treasury
18. Revolutionary War general at Fort Stanwix
20. Mother of Abraham Lincoln
21. Twenty-third president
23. Heroine of the battle of Monmouth during the American Revolution

© 1993 by The Center for Applied Research in Education

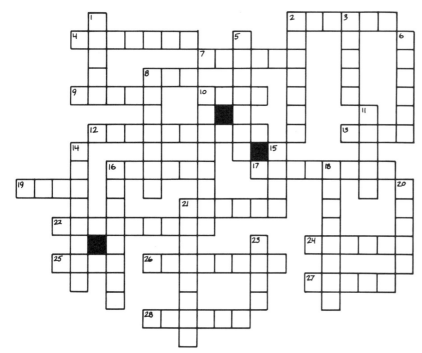

Name _____ Date _____

85. FAMOUS AMERICAN NAMES BEGINNING WITH J

ACROSS: _____

3. Seventh president
4. Seventeenth president
5. Labor organizer known as "Mother"
7. Confederate general "Stonewall"

8. America's first golf hero
9. Third president
10. First Chief Justice of the Supreme Court
11. Thirty-sixth president

DOWN: _____

1. Captain of the ship *Bonhomme Richard*
2. "Great Society" president
3. 1988 Democratic presidential candidate
4. Heavyweight boxing champion, 1899–1905

6. "Old Hickory"
8. Made an unpopular treaty with Britain in 1794

86. FAMOUS AMERICAN NAMES BEGINNING WITH K

ACROSS:

3. George Washington's Secretary of War
5. Thirty-fifth president
6. Author of "containment policy" toward the Soviets
7. Civil rights leader slain in 1968
8. Presidential candidate assassinated in 1968
9. Founder of the National Grange

DOWN:

1. "New Frontier" president
2. Author of the "Star-Spangled Banner"
3. President Nixon's Secretary of State
4. Democratic presidential candidate in 1976
5. Mexican War general, "The Long Marcher"

Name ———————————————————— Date ————————————————

87. FAMOUS AMERICAN NAMES BEGINNING WITH L

ACROSS: ————————————————————————————————————

1. Cowboy "Deadwood Dick"
2. Confederate general in the Civil War
6. "What you farmers need to do is raise less corn and more hell"
7. Sixteenth president
8. First solo transatlantic airplane flight
9. Black Muslim leader Malcolm X

12. Wisconsin reform governor, "Fighting Bob"
14. Nixon's aide involved with the Watergate scandal
15. Kansas governor and presidential candidate

DOWN: ——————————————————————————————————————

1. Founder of the first women's college
2. Confederate general who surrendered at Appomattox
3. Assassinated Louisiana governor
4. "Henry Ford of the housing industry"
5. "The Kingfish"
6. Editor of *Vanity Fair*
7. Massachusetts senator opposed to the League of Nations

9. Author of *Main Street*
10. Explorer of the Louisiana Territory
11. President of the United Mine Workers Union
12. Founder of Mount Holyoke Female Seminary
13. "You have lost but your left arm, while I have lost my right"

88. FAMOUS AMERICAN NAMES BEGINNING WITH M

ACROSS:

4. Chief Justice appointed by President John Adams
5. Colonial minister in Massachusetts
9. President Kennedy's Secretary of Defense
10. Fifth president
12. Spokeswoman for abolition
14. Inventor of the mechanical reaper
16. Union general, "Tardy George"
18. Inventor of the Linotype machine
19. Immigrant who became a world-famous comedian
20. Fourth president
22. Vice president of President Carter
23. First black Supreme Court Justice
25. 1972 Democratic presidential candidate

DOWN:

1. Inventor of the telegraph
2. Indian chief in the Massachusetts colony
3. Revolutionary War leader, "The Swamp Fox"
6. Famous news broadcaster in World War II
7. "Father of American education"
8. World War II general, "I shall return"
10. Wampanoag Indian chief, "King Philip"
11. Twenty-fifth president
13. Union general at the battle of Gettysburg
14. Nixon's aide involved with the Watergate scandal
15. First black to attend the University of Mississippi
17. The nation's leading financier in 1895
20. 1960's anthropologist
21. Revolutionary War Superintendent of Finance
24. Suffragette who attended the World's Antislavery Convention in London in 1840

89. FAMOUS AMERICAN NAMES BEGINNING WITH N

ACROSS: _____

3. Author of *Unsafe at Any Speed*
5. Inventor of the cast-iron plow
6. New York colonial ruler sent back to England by Jacob Leisler's revolt

7. Thirty-seventh president

DOWN: _____

1. Commander of the "Godspeed" voyage to Virginia
2. North Dakota senator who investigated the causes of World War I
3. World War II naval leader

4. Nebraska congressman who limited the power of House Speaker "Uncle Joe" Cannon
5. Political cartoonist in the 1800's

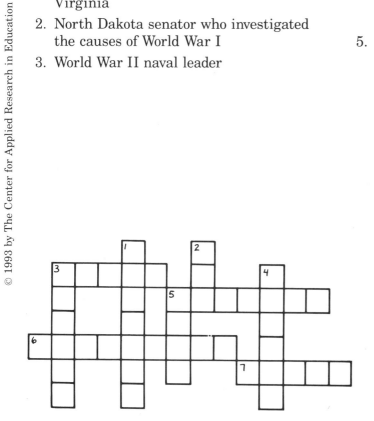

Name _____ Date _____

90. FAMOUS AMERICAN NAMES BEGINNING WITH O

ACROSS: _____

3. New York magazine editor who termed the phrase "manifest destiny"

5. Director of the Los Alamos Bomb Project

6. Assassin of President Kennedy

7. First woman Supreme Court Justice

8. President Cleveland's Attorney General

DOWN: _____

1. Chief of the Seminole Indians of Florida

2. Boston stamp collector forced to resist by the colonists

4. Founder of the colony of Georgia

91. FAMOUS AMERICAN NAMES BEGINNING WITH P

ACROSS:

2. Lady who refused to give up her seat on a Montgomery bus
5. "We have met the enemy and they are ours"
7. Author of *Common Sense*
9. One of the founders of the Women's Party
10. Fourteenth president
11. Founder of a detective agency
12. World War I general
14. Algonquin Indian chief in the Virginia colony
15. First female Cabinet member
16. U.S. spy shot down over the Soviet Union
19. Author of the New Jersey Plan for the Constitution
21. Precinct captain for the Tammany Hall political machine in New York City
22. Grand Master Workman of the Knights of Labor

DOWN:

1. 1950's rock-and-roll singer
2. Inventor of the railroad sleeping car
3. "You ain't nothin' but a hound dog"
4. U.S. ambassador who made a treaty with Spain in 1795
5. Confederate general in the battle of Gettysburg
6. New York minister who exposed police corruption in 1892
7. Editor of the *New York World*
8. Founder of the colony of Pennsylvania
10. World War II general
13. First African-American to serve as chairman of the Joint Chiefs of Staff
17. U.S. tank commander in World War II
18. U-2 spy pilot
19. Eleventh president
20. War of 1812 naval leader
22. Mexican War president

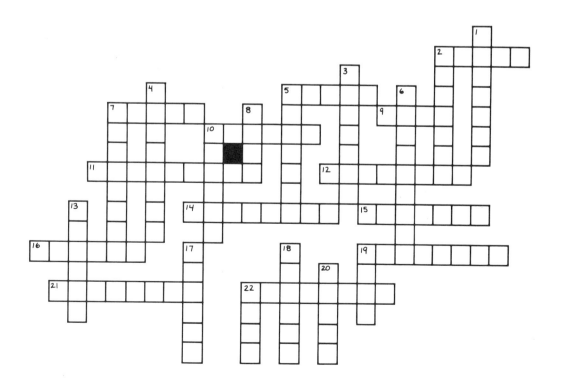

92. FAMOUS AMERICAN NAMES BEGINNING WITH R

ACROSS: _____

3. Twenty-sixth president
4. Virginia colonist who married Pocahontas
5. American photographer, 1902
10. Executed in 1953 for spying
11. Founder of Roanoke Island
12. American artist, 1897
13. Assassin of Martin Luther King, Jr.
15. "The British are coming"
18. American industrialist and philanthropist
19. Leader of the medical team that rid Cuba of yellow fever
20. Army surgeon in the Spanish-American War
21. Thirty-second president
22. One of the founders of the Committee for Industrial Organization
23. Author of the Virginia Plan for the Constitution
24. President Kennedy's Secretary of State

DOWN: _____

1. First black professional baseball player
2. American artist
3. "The Sultan of Swat"
4. First American baseball hero
5. Fortieth president
6. "First Lady of the World"
7. Doctor who rid Cuba of yellow fever
8. President Nixon's Attorney General
9. Author of How the Other Half Lives
12. First woman elected to the House of Representatives
14. Black elected to the Senate after the Civil War
16. Colonist who introduced tobacco into Virginia
17. American artist
20. Assassin of Martin Luther King, Jr.

Name _____ Date _____

93. FAMOUS AMERICAN NAMES BEGINNING WITH S

ACROSS:

2. Federal judge in the Watergate hearings
5. Leader of the Jamestown settlement
6. Slave who sued for his freedom
7. First person to steal one million dollars from the U.S. government
9. Vice president of the Confederate States of America
10. Leader of the Radical Republican Reconstructionists
13. Indian who helped the New England settlers
14. First heavyweight boxing champion, "the Boston Strong Boy"

17. "No work, no eat"
18. Union general who made the "March to the sea"
19. World War I naval leader
21. Mexican War general
22. Indian guide of Lewis and Clark
23. Author of *Uncle Tom's Cabin*
24. Head of the Peace Corps
25. "Old Fuss and Feathers"
26. Leader of the Plymouth settlers
27. Persian Gulf War general
28. Indian who helped the New England settlers

DOWN:

1. Farmers' rebellion in Massachusetts
2. Inventor of the typewriter
3. Leader of a colonial rebellion in 1786
4. Female antislavery leader
5. "War is hell"
7. Teacher who was sued for teaching evolution
8. Reporter who searched for Dr. Livingstone in Africa
11. Naval leader in the Spanish-American War
12. Author of *The Jungle*

14. Improved the sewing machine
15. Indian leader at the battle of Little Big Horn
16. Secretary of State who purchased Alaska
18. "Father of the American factory system"
20. Mexican War general
21. Leader of the National Labor Union
23. Abolitionist author
24. Colonial rebellion in Springfield, Massachusetts

Name ————————————————————— Date —————————————

94. FAMOUS AMERICAN NAMES BEGINNING WITH T

ACROSS: —————————————————————————————

2. Pen name of Samuel Clemens
3. Thirty-third president
4. Sponsor of an amendment to gradually ban slavery
6. Tenth president
7. Chief Justice during the Dred Scott Decision

11. Shawnee Indian chief
12. Leader of a slave rebellion in Virginia
13. Twelfth president
14. Political "boss" of New York City
15. "The buck stops here"

DOWN: —————————————————————————————

1. Author of *History of the Standard Oil Company*
2. Tennis hero, "Big Bill"
3. Tammany Hall corrupt politician
4. Twenty-seventh president
5. First vice president to succeed to the president upon the death of his predecessor

8. South Carolina Dixiecrat
9. Author of *The Duty of Civil Disobedience*
10. 1948 States' Rights Party presidential candidate

© 1993 by The Center for Applied Research in Education

Name _____   Date _____

95. FAMOUS AMERICAN NAMES BEGINNING WITH W

ACROSS: _____

1. Founder of the five-and-ten cents store
4. "Steer clear of permanent alliances"
8. Twenty-eighth president
9. Founder of the colony of Rhode Island
11. Inventor of the cotton gin
14. Leader of the Bonus Army March on Washington in 1945

15. Philadelphia merchant who first installed arc lights
16. Populist Party leader from Georgia
17. American general at the battle of Fallen Timbers, "Mad Anthony"
18. Author of the first American dictionary

DOWN: _____

2. New York senator whose act listed "unfair labor practices"
3. Republican candidate who lost to FDR in 1940
5. First president
6. Leader of the Massachusetts Bay Colony
7. Governor of the Louisiana Territory

8. Famous American poet
10. Black colonial poet
12. 1972 presidential candidate paralyzed in an assassination attempt
13. "Liberty and Union, now and forever, one and inseparable!"

96. VOCABULARY WORDS IN AMERICAN HISTORY—I

ACROSS:

2. Gold and silver coins
4. Having support from both major political parties
5. Overall plan, especially relating to a military operation
6. Lying in court while testifying under oath
8. Names of union members that are circulated among company owners who then refuse to hire those workers
12. Northerner who moved south to take advantage of unsettled economic and political conditions after the Civil War
15. Official and regular record of population facts
16. Lender to whom money is owed
18. Skill in conducting relations between people or nations
19. Easing of Cold War tensions between the United States and Soviet Union
20. One who believed in the end of slavery
23. Sparsely populated country area
26. Country that governs itself but relies on the defense system of a stronger nation
27. Refusal to buy, sell, or use a good or service
30. Policy of not taking sides in a war
32. Farmer who pays his rent in cash
33. Power of an executive to refuse to sign a bill
34. Ruler who possesses power superior to all others
35. Sales tax on the manufacture, sale, or consumption of goods produced within a nation
36. Person who sold illegal liquor during Prohibition
37. President's power to prevent a bill from becoming law
38. Militia in colonial America, who were prepared to assemble at a moment's notice
41. Compulsory military service
43. Wooden ships built during the Civil War that were fortified with armor
44. Payment for an item that is spread out over regular, timed intervals
47. Any object made by people
48. Paper money issued by the federal government
50. To hear both sides of a dispute and render a judgment
54. Group organized for the establishment of a monopoly by price-fixing
55. Hired soldiers who serve in a foreign army
56. Study of the production, distribution, and consumption of goods
57. Legislature having two houses
58. Country joined with another for common purposes
59. Business unit in which several companies function as one by informally agreeing to jointly-made decisions

DOWN:

1. Opinion that opposes an official religious view
3. Group of nations or colonies under one sovereign power
4. Government official or worker
7. Use of force to achieve results
9. Closing a business temporarily so that workers will eventually yield to company demands
10. To block Soviet attempts to expansion anywhere in the world
11. Association of workers to promote their interests
12. Meeting of leaders of a political party to decide policy or pick candidates
13. Entire surroundings that affect an individual
14. Borrower who owes money to others
17. Process of being set free from slavery
21. Tactic whereby demonstrators occupy a public facility until it is desegregated
22. Exemption from the jurisdiction of local authority
24. Workers skilled in a particular craft
25. Revolutionary War soldiers
28. Makeshift living area erected by the homeless during the Great Depression
29. Severe economic slump
31. Theory that argues that human beings evolved from life forms
39. Medical insurance for the elderly paid through Social Security
40. Unnecessary government jobs or programs
42. Official permit granted by a ruler to a person or group
43. Entry into a new nation for the purpose of permanent settlement
45. Combination of corporations to reduce competition
46. Economic condition in which inflation accompanies increased unemployment
49. Group that advises the president
51. The lack of any type of government
52. Written or illustrated material that injures someone's reputation through false statements
53. Workers who cross strike lines to work

96. Vocabulary Words in American History—I

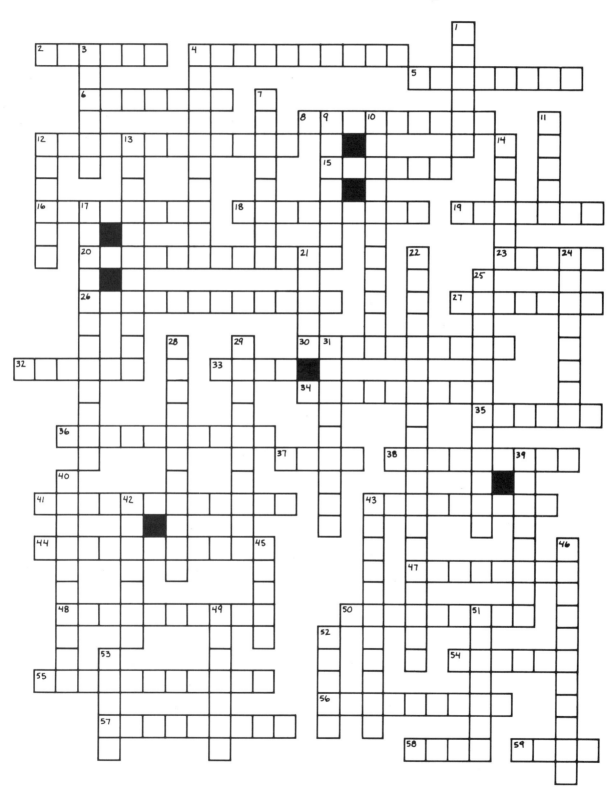

97. VOCABULARY WORDS IN AMERICAN HISTORY—II

ACROSS:

2. One who supports rapid change rather than gradual reform
4. Procedure to remove elected officials from office before their terms are completed
10. Broad-wheeled wagons used by pioneers to cross the prairie
11. Person devoted to helping others
14. Agricultural arrangement in which farm workers were loaned equipment in exchange for a portion of their harvest
17. Period of enormous social upheaval following the Civil War
18. Deliberate extermination of a group of people
19. Court order demanding that a certain action be done
21. Smuggled goods
23. Practice of spying
26. A black who moved from the post-Reconstruction South to Kansas
30. Declaration of a particular position
31. Meeting of political party leaders before a regular meeting of the party

33. Authorized delay or postponement
35. Increase in prices accompanied by a decline in the purchasing power of money
36. To release from military service at the end of a war
37. Money gained in the sale of an item after costs are deducted
43. Partial refund from a bill
44. Period when alcoholic beverages were illegal in the United States
45. Power of a president to prevent a bill from becoming law
47. Military supplies, including weapons and ammunition
48. Process whereby a state declares a federal law null and void
49. Workers who cross strike lines to work
50. Bias toward people of another race, sex, or religion
51. Document bearing the signatures of supporters
52. Specified food allotment, usually in reference to wartime

DOWN:

1. Person whose political beliefs favor experimentation and change
3. Pardon of offenses committed against a government
5. Breed of cattle well-suited to long cattle drives
6. Term used for a white Southerner who joined the Republican party after the Civil War
7. Refusal to work by union members
8. Closing a nation's ports to commercial shipping
9. Practice of rewarding political supporters with a job
12. Process of petitioning a legislature to introduce a bill
13. Leaving one's country to seek political asylum in another nation
15. Owner of a private ship commissioned by a government to attack enemy ships
16. Organization of farmers for social and economic benefits
20. Multi-family apartment often with unsafe and overcrowded conditions
22. Incorporation of immigrants into American life

24. Privilege accorded to a person for length of service on the job
25. Referring to a city or town with a high population
27. Informal agreement between similar companies to function as one
28. Science of human society and social relations
29. Region administered by victorious Allied nations after World War I
32. Solution to a deadlock in which each side gives up some demands
34. Revision or addition to a constitution
38. To charge a government official with a crime in office
39. Opponent of American independence who maintained allegiance to Britain during the Revolutionary War
40. Fee required of voters (*two words*)
41. Recorded events of the past
42. Position or rank in society
46. Regular record of population facts, also used to determine the number of seats in the House of Representatives for each state

Name _____   Date _____

97. Vocabulary Words in American History—II

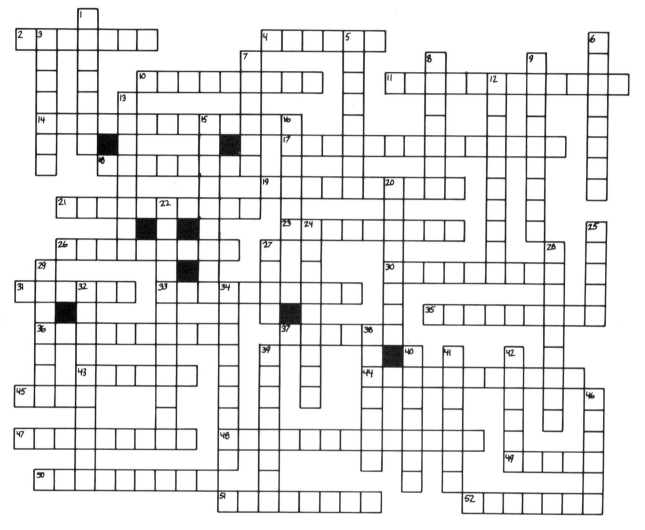

98. VOCABULARY WORDS IN AMERICAN HISTORY—III

ACROSS:

4. To remove elected officials before their term expires
9. Believer in traditional politics and minimum government
10. Victorious countries in World War II
14. To act as a go-between to settle a dispute
15. Extended speech in Congress to delay voting on a bill
16. Desire to help people through gifts and deeds
18. Exclusive control of a certain product in a market
19. Country joined with another for common purposes
21. Required payment to finance government operations
24. Indiscriminate killing
25. Practice of forcing men into military service
33. To discuss or bargain to achieve agreement
34. Temporary decline in business activity
35. Worker who refuses to join a union
37. Nation whose affairs are controlled by a stronger power
38. Compensation, especially for war damages
41. Penalties, usually measures to force another nation to change its actions
42. Private meeting of political party leaders
43. To cast a ballot for a political candidate
45. Practical application of scientific knowledge
47. Guerrillas opposing the Sandinista government in Nicaragua
49. Regular record of population facts
50. Engagement in a risky business venture with hope of future profits
51. Easing of tensions between nations
52. Summons that orders a person to appear in court
53. Association of workers to promote and protect their welfare
54. Northerners who moved south after the Civil War to seek political or economic gain
55. Legislature having only one house

DOWN:

1. Northern democrat who opposed the Civil War
2. Study of the Earth's landforms, climate, water, etc.
3. Prejudice in treatment
5. Written material that is damaging or false
6. Group organized to obtain a monopoly by price-fixing
7. Demonstration by union workers on strike
8. To approve a course of action
11. One's ancestors, family, and blood relatives
12. Transformation from hand-made production to machines
13. Supplies that can meet important needs
15. Young woman of the 1920's
17. One who supports middle-of-the-road politics
20. Information that is spread to further one's cause
22. Closing a nation's ports to commercial shipping
23. Partial refund from a bill
24. Journalist who reports social injustices
26. The right to vote
27. Area of public land set aside for Native Americans
28. Process in which voters approve or reject a bill
29. Require races to remain separate from each other
30. Executive's refusal to sign a bill
31. Informal agreement by several companies to obey joint decisions
32. Withdrawal of a state from the Union
36. Nation in which power is held by voting citizens
39. Association of workers
40. Violent overthrow of a government
41. Place where liquor was sold illegally during Prohibition
42. Written permit granted by a ruler
44. Small religious group formed from larger established churches
46. Area of municipalities surrounding a city
48. Demonstration that occupies a facility until it is desegregated
52. Worker who crosses strike lines to work

98. Vocabulary Words in American History—III

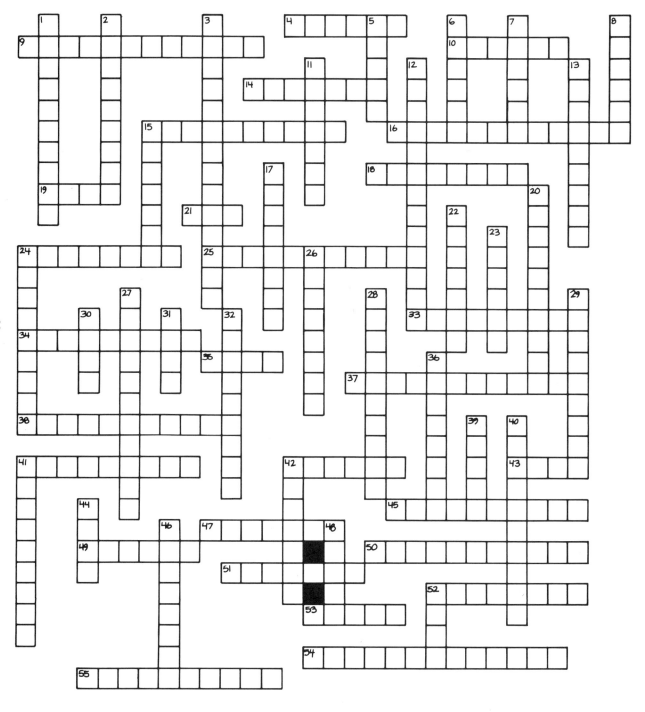

Name _____   Date _____

99. IMPORTANT YEARS IN AMERICAN HISTORY—I

ACROSS:

2. Prohibition began
4. Columbus discovered America
5. U.S. entered World War I
7. Englishman, John Cabot, reached America
9. Prohibition ended
10. First transcontinental railroad was completed
12. Civil Rights Act was passed
13. Camp David Accord was signed
14. Navigation Act was passed on the colonies
15. Articles of Confederation passed

17. Income tax became law
20. First U.S. satellite put into orbit
21. Charles Lindbergh flew the Atlantic
22. U.S. purchased Alaska
24. French and Indian War ended
25. Martin Luther King, Jr. was assassinated
26. John Marshall was appointed Chief Justice
28. Texas was founded by Stephen Austin
29. Noah Webster published his dictionary
30. Sugar Act was passed on the colonies

DOWN:

1. Korean War ended
2. Mexican War began
3. Battle of Bunker Hill
4. U.S. obtained Florida
5. Fundamental Orders of Connecticut
6. War of 1812 ended
8. Roger Williams settled Rhode Island
11. President Kennedy was assassinated
12. Eighteen-year-olds gained the right to vote
13. First slaves were brought to the colonies

14. King Philip's War
16. U.S. bought the Virgin Islands
18. College of William and Mary founded
19. U.S. Navy was established
21. William Penn settled Pennsylvania
23. Spanish-American War
24. World War I ended
25. World War I began
27. President Nixon resigned

Name _____ Date _____

100. IMPORTANT YEARS IN AMERICAN HISTORY—II

ACROSS:

4. William Jennings Bryan made his famous "cross of gold" speech
5. House of Burgesses met
7. Thomas Hooker settled Connecticut
8. Sir Walter Raleigh settled Roanoke Island
9. Attempted assassination of Ronald Reagan
11. Vietnam War ended
12. Mexican War ended
13. Great Depression began
14. Panama Canal opened

16. U.S. astronauts landed on the moon
18. President Garfield was assassinated
20. NATO was formed
21. U.S. troops sent to Vietnam
22. *Uncle Tom's Cabin* was published
23. Lord Baltimore settled Maryland
29. First space shuttle flight
30. First powered airplane flight
31. Blacks gained the right to vote
32. U.S. boycotted the Olympic Games

DOWN:

1. President McKinley was assassinated
2. Poll tax abolished
3. Yale University founded
4. Robert F. Kennedy was assassinated
5. Maryland Toleration Act passed
6. First U.S. female astronaut in space
7. President Andrew Johnson was impeached
10. XYZ Affair with France
11. Gold rush to California
12. Jamestown settlement was started
13. Bill of Rights was added to the Constitution
14. Hawaii became the fiftieth state

15. World War II began
17. President Lincoln was assassinated
19. Pilgrims landed in Massachusetts
20. First U.S. astronaut orbited the earth
22. First Thanksgiving celebration
24. Samuel Morse developed the telegraph
25. President William Henry Harrison died in office
26. Women gained the right to vote
27. British surrendered at Yorktown
28. Korean War started

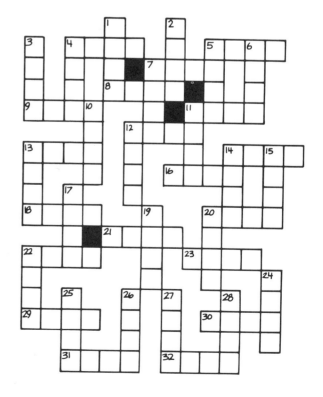

101. IMPORTANT YEARS IN AMERICAN HISTORY—III

ACROSS:

3. Civil War began
4. Intolerable Acts passed on the colonies
8. Commodore Perry went to Japan
10. Treaty of Paris ended the American Revolution
12. Articles of Confederation passed
14. Mayflower Compact
15. Dred Scott decision
16. Quartering Act passed on the colonies
18. First transcontinental airplane flight
20. First Thanksgiving
22. John Brown raided Harper's Ferry
23. Eighteen-year-olds gained the right to vote
25. America declared independence
28. Lincoln-Douglas debates
29. War of 1812 ended
30. Whiskey Rebellion
34. Income tax amendment passed
36. Tea Act passed on the colonies
38. U.S. Supreme Court established
39. Brown v. Board of Education
40. U.S. celebrated its bicentennial
41. Cuban Missile Crisis
42. John Adams died
43. Thomas Paine wrote *Common Sense*
44. Constitution was passed
45. Erie Canal opened
47. Thomas Jefferson died
50. Battle of Monitor vs. Merrimac
51. Molasses Act passed on the colonies
52. Atomic bombs dropped on Japan
53. Robert Fulton invented the steamboat
54. World War II ended
55. Emancipation Proclamation
56. French and Indian War started

DOWN:

1. Louisiana Purchase
2. First national census was taken
3. Battles of Lexington and Concord
4. Medicare was established
5. Gold rush to California
6. Missouri Compromise
7. U.S. obtained Florida
9. Marbury v. Madison
10. First Continental Congress met
11. Townshend Acts passed on the Colonies
13. Shays' Rebellion
14. The Pequot War
17. Albany Plan of Union proposed
19. Indians received U.S. citizenship
21. George Washington became the first president
23. Pennsylvania was chartered
24. Texas declared independence
26. Columbia University founded
27. Bacon's Rebellion
31. Eli Whitney invented the cotton gin
32. Northwest Ordinance
33. U.S. entered World War I
34. Stamp Act passed on the colonies
35. U.S. joined the United Nations
36. Monroe Doctrine passed
37. President Ford pardoned former President Nixon
42. Women gained the right to vote
43. Slavery was abolished
44. Civil War ended
45. Boston Tea Party
46. Jamestown was founded
47. Harvard University founded
48. Social Security Act passed
49. Japanese attacked Pearl Harbor

101. Important Years in American History—III

Answer Keys

1. The First Americans

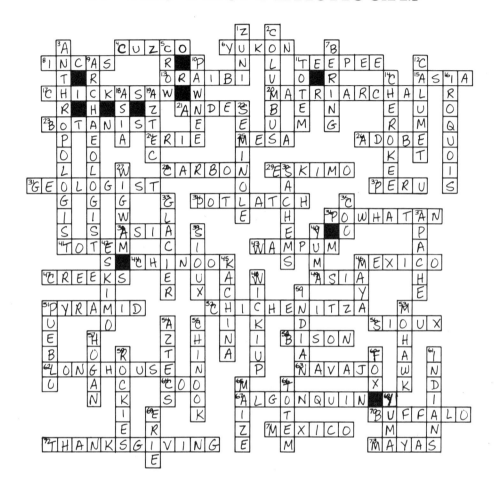

2. Spanish Exploration in the New World

3. French Exploration in the New World

4. English Exploration in the New World

5. The First American Settlements

6. The Original Thirteen Colonies

7. The French and Indian War

8. The Idea of Liberty

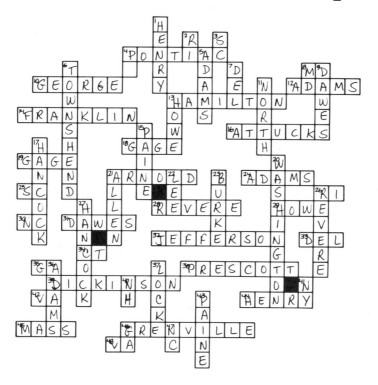

9. The Declaration of Independence

10. The American Revolutionary War

11. Men and Women of the American Revolution

12. Battles of the American Revolution

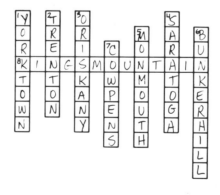

13. The Articles of Confederation

14. The Constitution

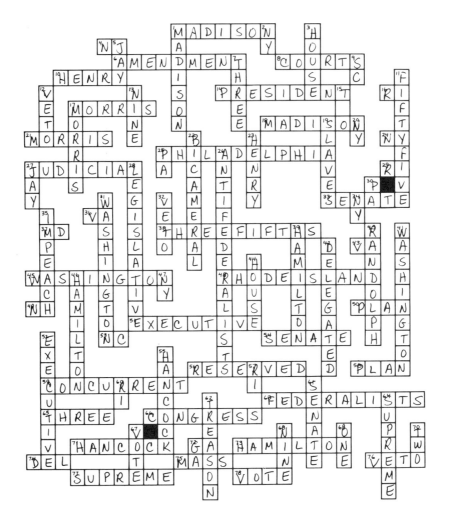

15. The Legislative Branch

16. The Executive Branch

17. The Judicial Branch

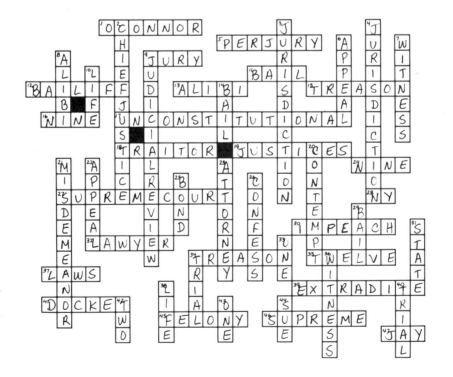

18. The Bill of Rights

19. Amendments to the Constitution

20. Our Founding Fathers

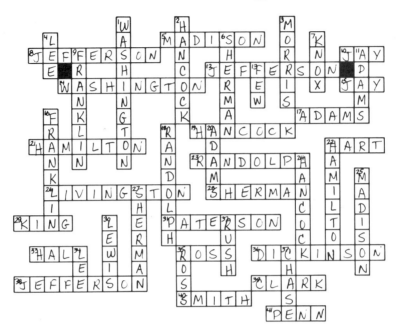

21. The First Presidency

22. The First Cabinet

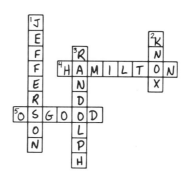

23. The Louisiana Purchase

24. The War of 1812

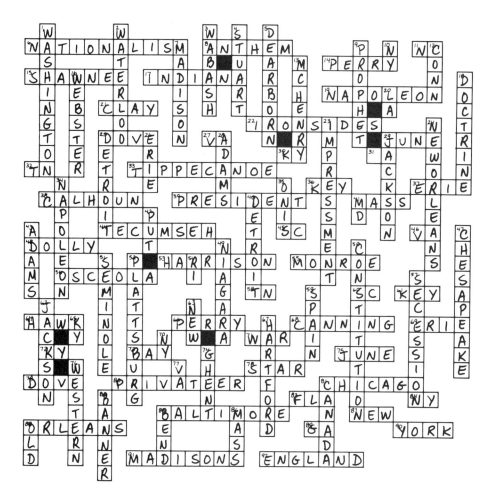

25. The Era of Good Feelings

26. The Jacksonian Period

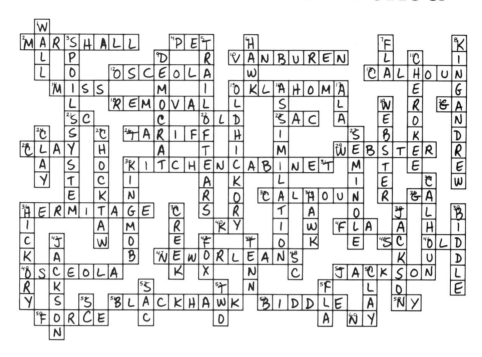

27. Inventors and Reformers

28. The Mexican War

29. Manifest Destiny

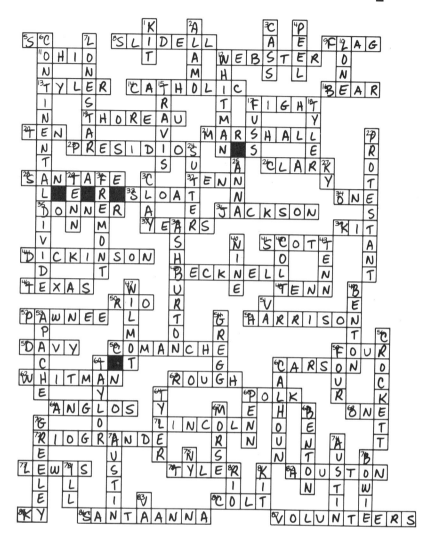

30. The Civil War

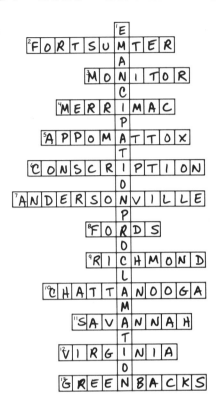

31. Battles of the Civil War

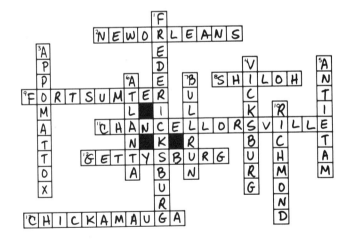

32. Men and Women of the Civil War

33. Southern Reconstruction

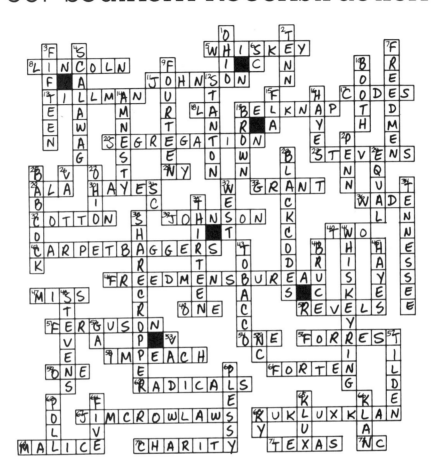

34. The Old West

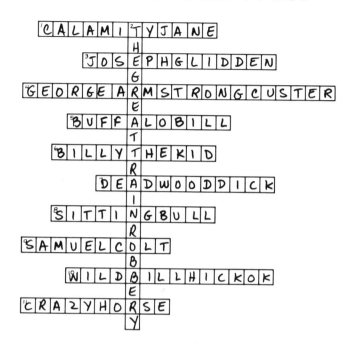

35. American Indians

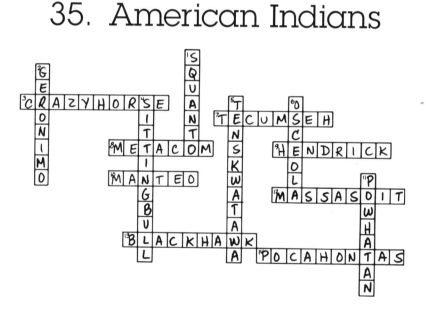

36. A New Industrial Age

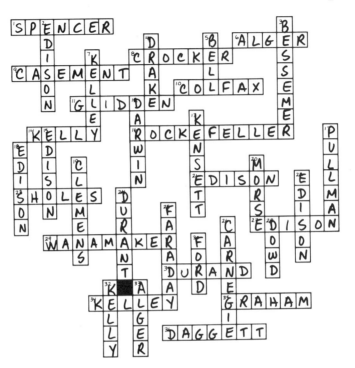

37. Cities and Big Business

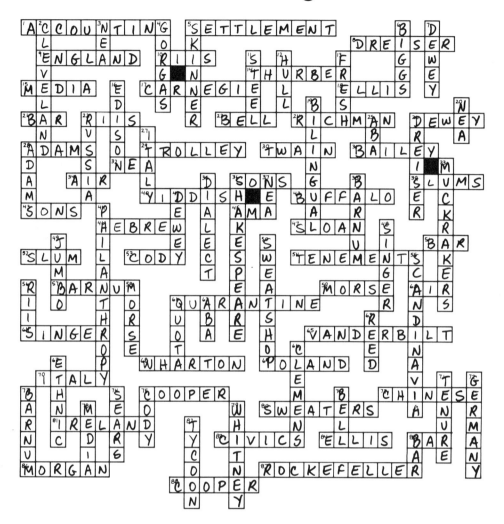

38. Workers and Unions

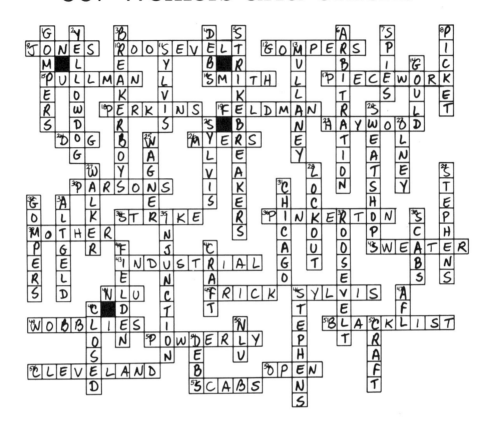

39. The Progressive Era

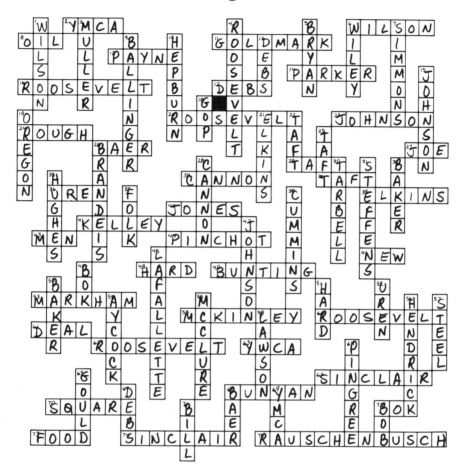

40. The Gilded Age

41. The Spanish-American War

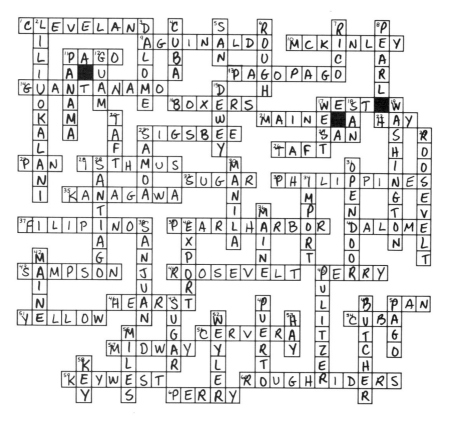

42. The Panama Canal

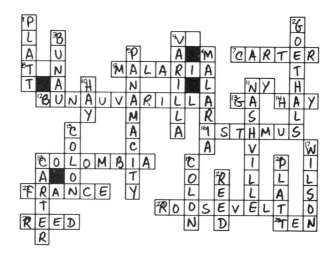

43. World War I

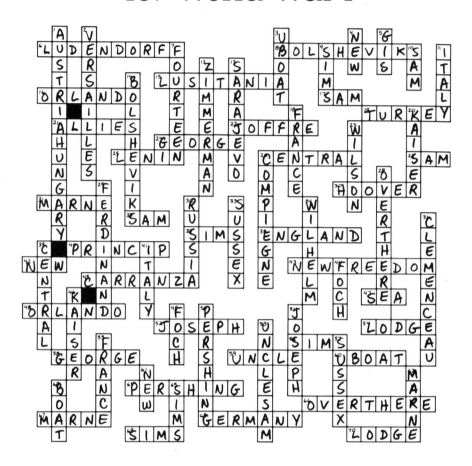

44. The Roaring 20's and the Great Depression

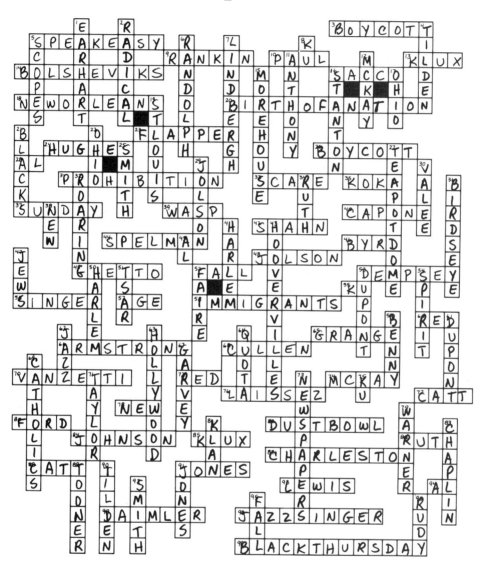

45. The New Deal

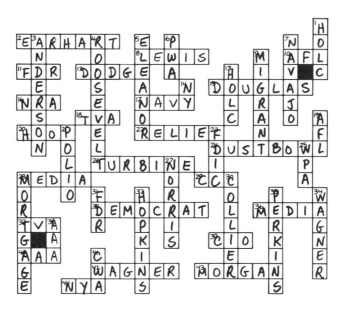

46. New Deal Abbreviations

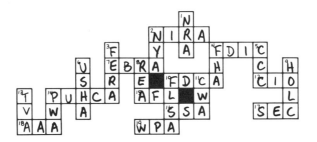

47. World War II

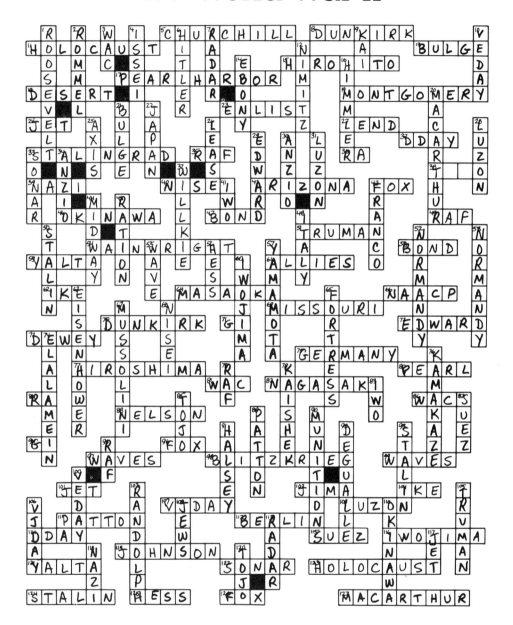

48. Post World War II

49. The 1950's

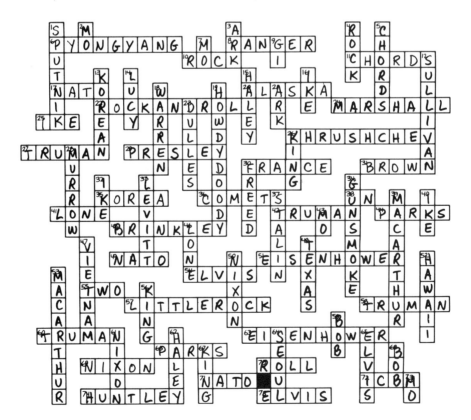

50. The 1960's

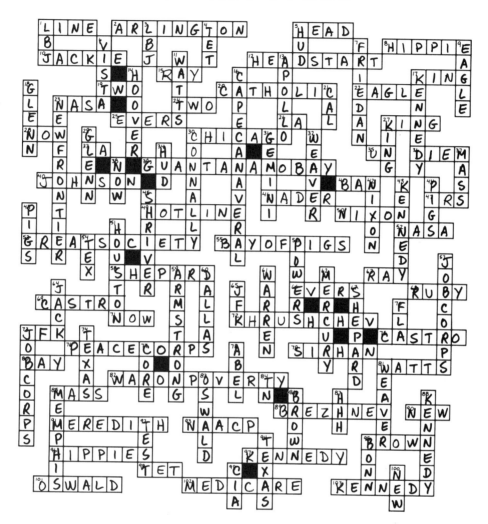

51. The 1970's

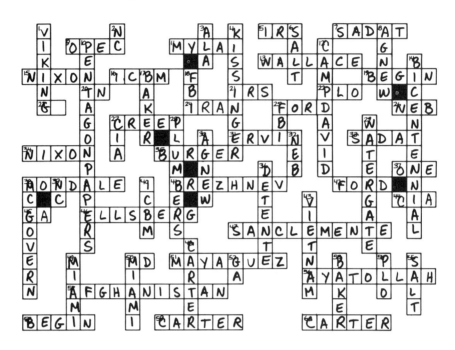

52. The 1980's

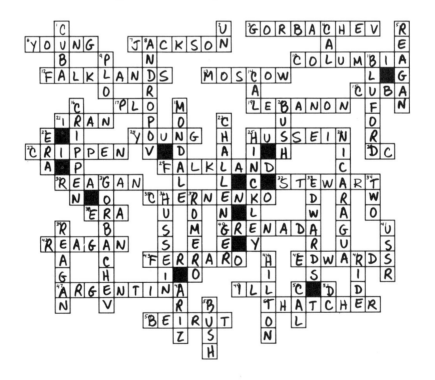

53. Capital Cities of the United States

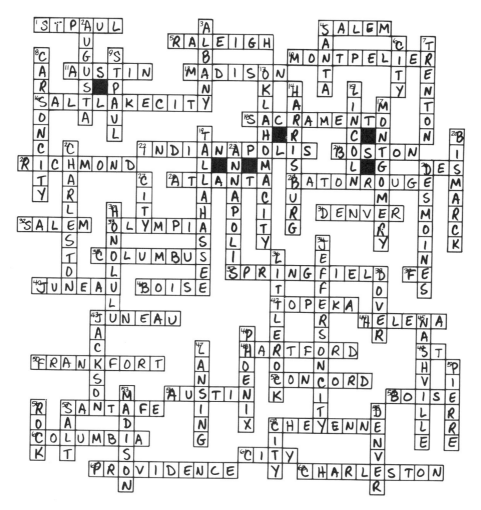

54. Mountains and Rivers of the United States

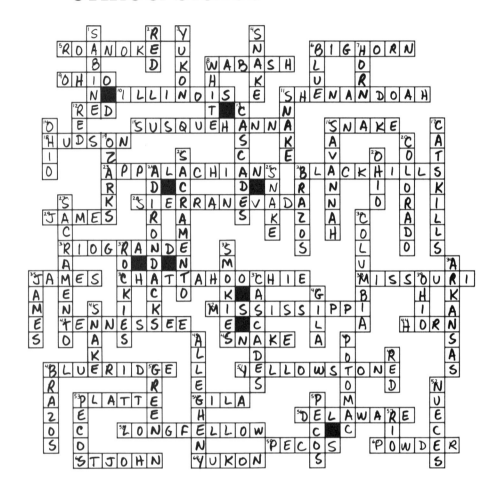

55. State Flowers

56. State Birds

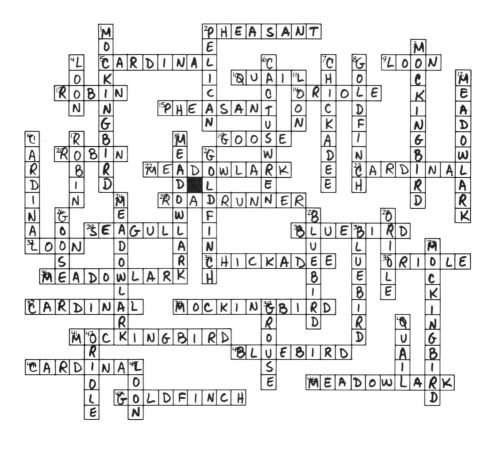

57. State Nicknames

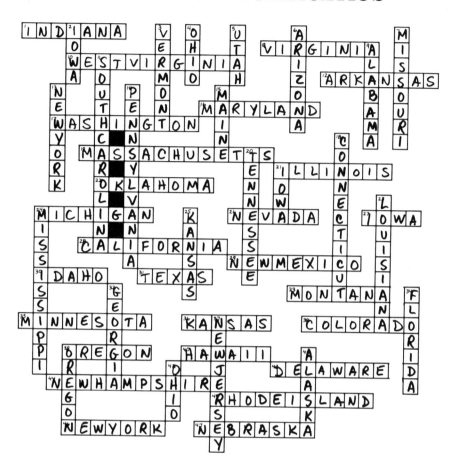

58. Presidential Trivia

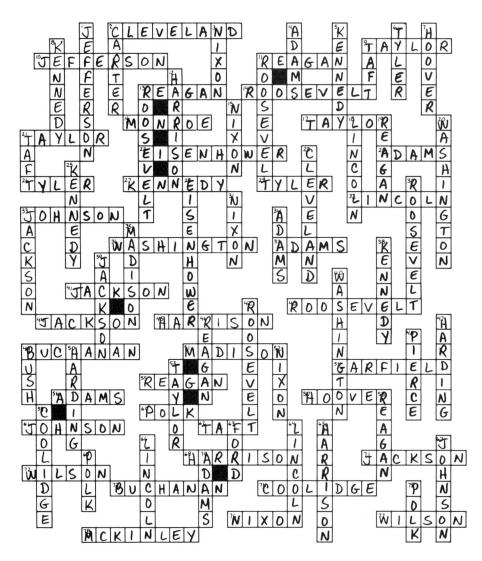

59. Presidential Quotations

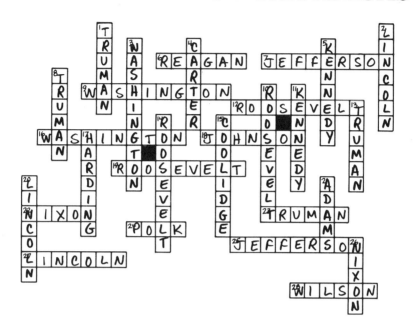

60. Presidential Nicknames

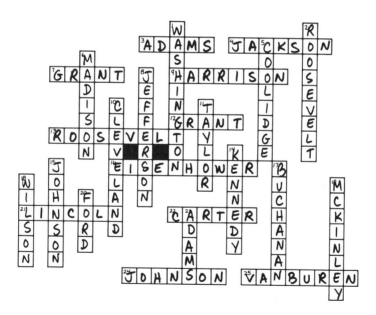

61. Presidential Birthplaces

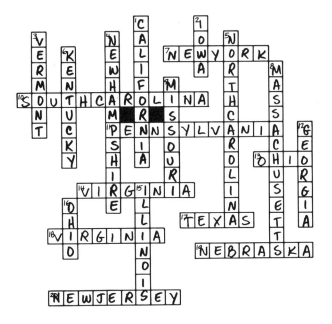

62. Vice Presidents

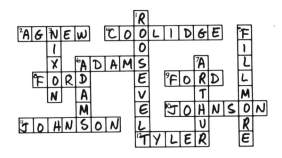

63. Administration Nicknames

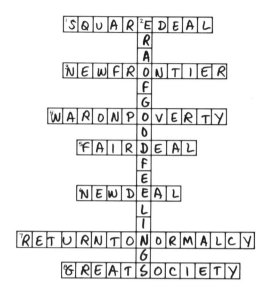

64. Wartime Presidents

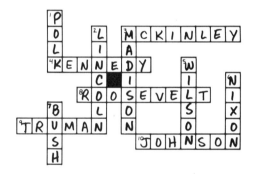

65. Losing Presidential Candidates

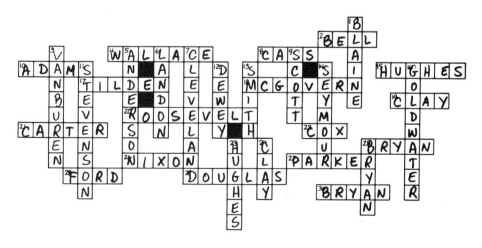

66. First Ladies

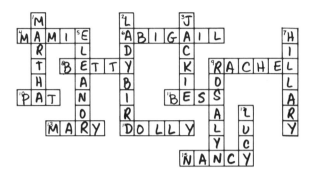

67. Chief Justices of the Supreme Court

68. Deaths and Assassinations

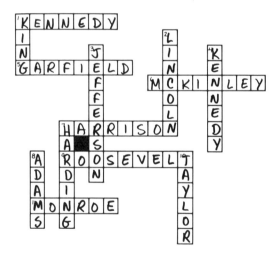

69. American Military Leaders

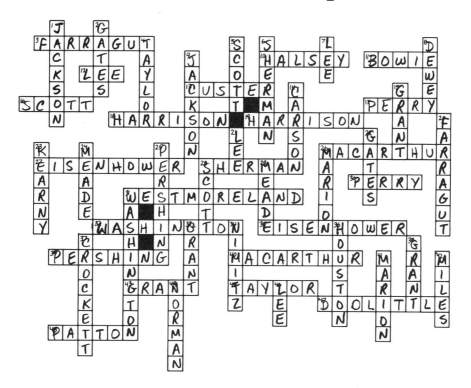

70. Americans in Space

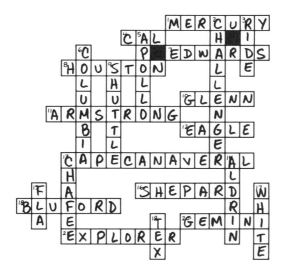

71. Women in American History

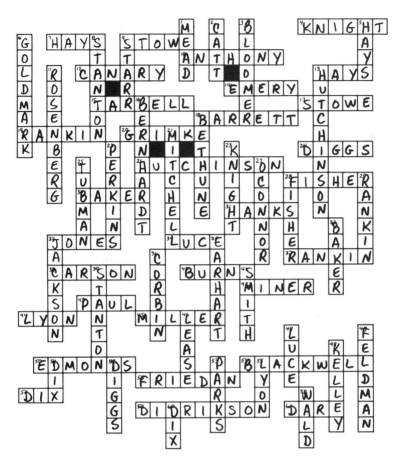

72. American Athletes

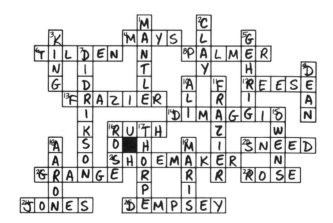

73. American Entertainers

74. Quotations in American History

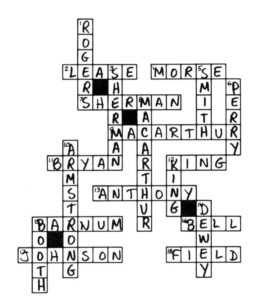

75. American Nicknames

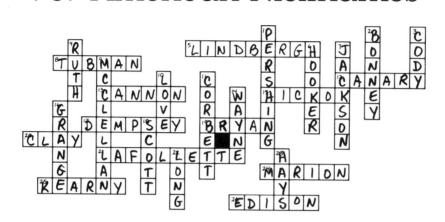

76. -Isms

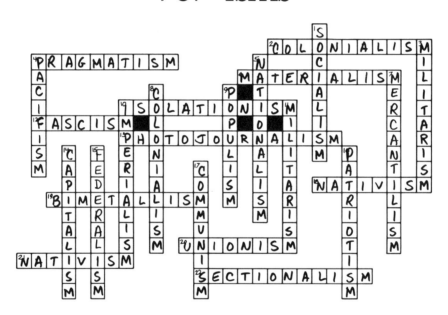

77. Famous American Names Beginning with A

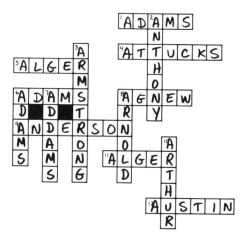

78. Famous American Names Beginning with B

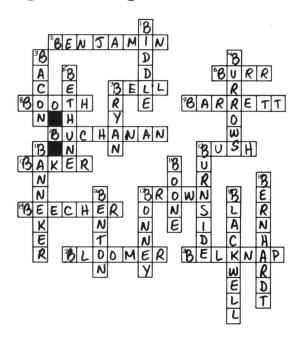

79. Famous American Names Beginning with C

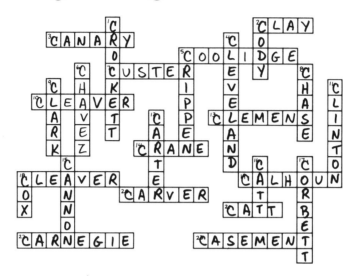

80. Famous American Names Beginning with D

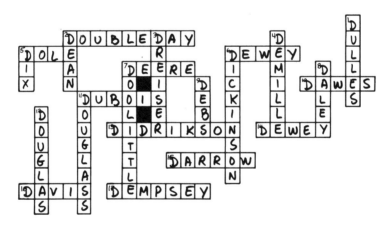

81. Famous American Names Beginning with E

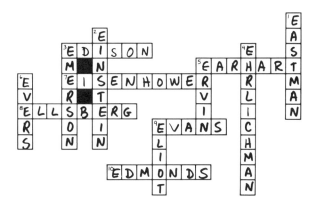

82. Famous American Names Beginning with F

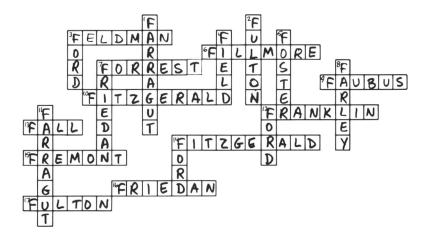

83. Famous American Names Beginning with G

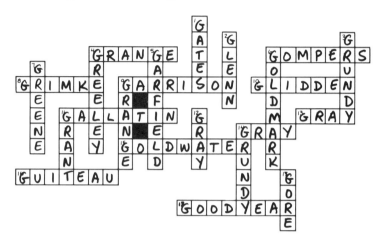

84. Famous American Names Beginning with H

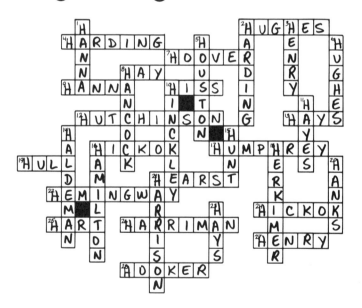

85. Famous American Names Beginning with J

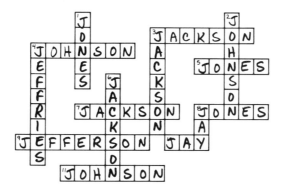

86. Famous American Names Beginning with K

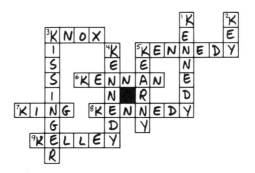

87. Famous American Names Beginning with L

88. Famous American Names Beginning with M

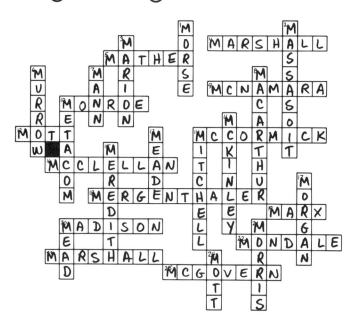

89. Famous American Names Beginning with N

90. Famous American Names Beginning with O

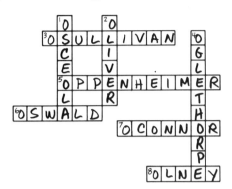

91. Famous American Names Beginning with P

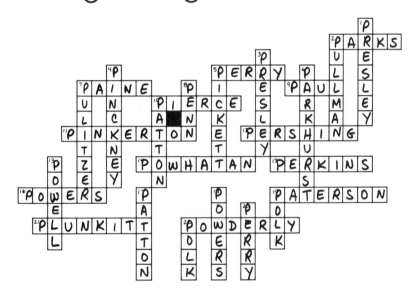

92. Famous American Names Beginning with R

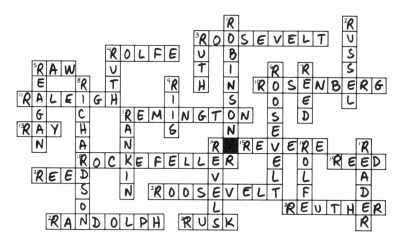

93. Famous American Names Beginning with S

94. Famous American Names Beginning with T

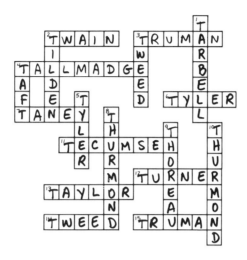

95. Famous American Names Beginning with W

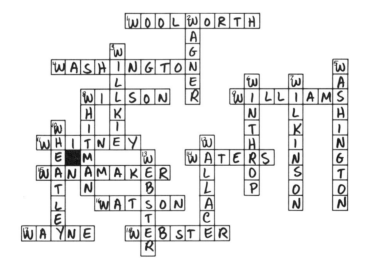

96. Vocabulary Words in American History—I

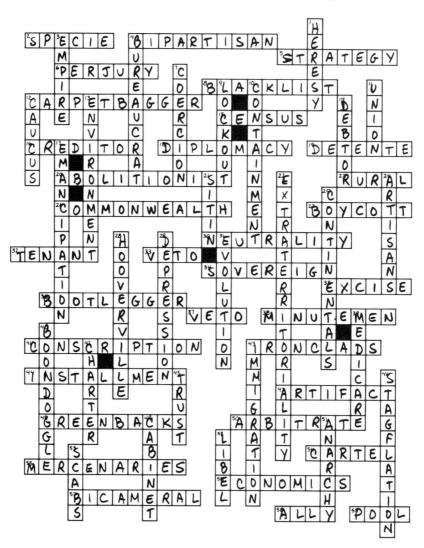

97. Vocabulary Words in American History—II

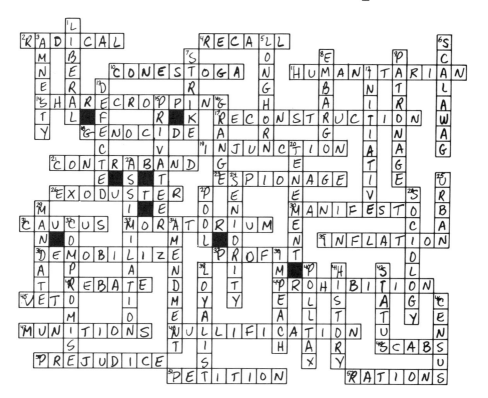

98. Vocabulary Words in American History—III

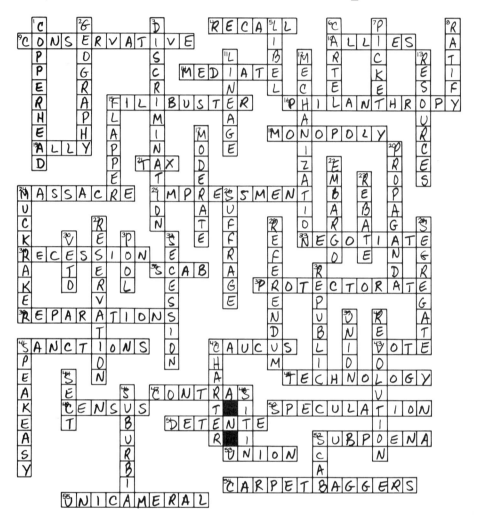

99. Important Years in American History—I

100. Important Years in American History—II

101. Important Years in American History—III